Glencoe McGraw-Hill

Chapter 7 Resource Masters

Precalculus

Mc Graw Hill Glencoe

StudentWorks Plus™ includes the entire Student Edition text along with the worksheets in this booklet.

TeacherWorks Plus™ includes all of the materials found in this booklet for viewing, printing, and editing.

Cover: Jason Reed/Photodisc/Getty Images

The McGraw-Hill Companies

 Glencoe

Copyright © by The McGraw-Hill Companies, Inc. All rights reserved. Permission is granted to reproduce the material contained herein on the condition that such materials be reproduced only for classroom use; be provided to students, teachers, and families without charge; and be used solely in conjunction with the *Glencoe Precalculus* program. Any other reproduction, for sale or other use, is expressly prohibited.

Send all inquiries to:
Glencoe/McGraw-Hill
8787 Orion Place
Columbus, OH 43240-4027

ISBN: 978-0-07-893808-5
MHID: 0-07-893808-2

Printed in the United States of America.

12 13 14 15 16 17 QVS 19 18 17 16 15

Contents

Teacher's Guide to Using the
Chapter 7 Resource Masters

The *Chapter 7 Resource Masters* includes the core materials needed for Chapter 7. These materials include worksheets, extensions, and assessment options. The answers for these pages appear at the back of this booklet.

Chapter Resources

Student-Built Glossary (pages 1–2) These masters are a student study tool that presents up to twenty of the key vocabulary terms from the chapter. Students are to record definitions and/or examples for each term. You may suggest that students highlight or star the terms with which they are not familiar. Give this to students before beginning *Lesson 7-1*. Encourage them to add these pages to their mathematics study notebooks. Remind them to complete the appropriate words as they study each lesson.

Anticipation Guide (pages 3–4) This master, presented in both English and Spanish, is a survey used before beginning the chapter to pinpoint what students may or may not know about the concepts in the chapter. Students will revisit this survey after they complete the chapter to see if their perceptions have changed.

Lesson Resources

Study Guide and Intervention These masters provide vocabulary, key concepts, additional worked-out examples and *Guided Practice* exercises to use as a reteaching activity. It can also be used in conjunction with the *Student Edition* as an instructional tool for students who have been absent.

Practice This master closely follows the types of problems found in the *Exercises* section of the *Student Edition* and includes word problems. Use as an additional practice option or as homework for second-day teaching of the lesson.

Word Problem Practice This master includes additional practice in solving word problems that apply to the concepts of the lesson. Use as an additional practice or as homework for second-day teaching of the lesson.

Enrichment These activities may extend the concepts of the lesson, offer an historical or multicultural look at the concepts, or widen students' perspectives on the mathematics they are learning. They are written for use with all levels of students.

Graphing Calculator, TI–Nspire, or Spreadsheet Activities These activities present ways in which technology can be used with the concepts in some lessons of this chapter. Use as an alternative approach to some concepts or as an integral part of your lesson presentation.

Assessment Options

The assessment masters in the *Chapter 7 Resource Masters* offer a wide range of assessment tools for formative (monitoring) assessment and summative (final) assessment.

Quizzes Four free-response quizzes offer assessment at appropriate intervals in the chapter.

Mid-Chapter Test This one-page test provides an option to assess the first half of the chapter. It parallels the timing of the *Mid-Chapter Quiz* in the *Student Edition* and includes both multiple-choice and free-response questions.

Vocabulary Test This test is suitable for all students. It includes a list of vocabulary words and questions to assess students' knowledge of those words. This can also be used in conjunction with one of the leveled chapter tests.

Leveled Chapter Tests

- *Form 1* contains multiple-choice questions and is intended for use with below grade level students.

- *Forms 2A and 2B* contain multiple-choice questions aimed at on grade level students. These tests are similar in format to offer comparable testing situations.

- *Forms 2C and 2D* contain free-response questions aimed at on grade level students. These tests are similar in format to offer comparable testing situations.

- *Form 3* is a free-response test for use with above grade level students.

All of the above mentioned tests include a free-response Bonus question.

Extended-Response Test Performance assessment tasks are suitable for all students. Sample answers are included for evaluation.

Standardized Test Practice These three pages are cumulative in nature. It includes two parts: multiple-choice questions with bubble-in answer format and short-answer free-response questions.

Answers

- The answers for the *Anticipation Guide* and *Lesson Resources* are provided as reduced pages.
- Full-size answer keys are provided for the assessment masters.

7 | Student-Built Glossary

This is an alphabetical list of the key vocabulary terms you will learn in Chapter 7. As you study the chapter, complete each term's definition or description. Remember to add the page number where you found the term. Add these pages to your Precalculus Study Notebook to review vocabulary at the end of the chapter.

Vocabulary Term	Found on Page	Definition/Description/Example
axis of symmetry		
conic section		
conjugate axis		
co-vertices		
degenerate conic		
directrix		
eccentricity		
ellipse		
focus (foci)		

(continued on the next page)

Chapter Resources

7 Student-Built Glossary

Vocabulary Term	Found on Page	Definition/Description/Example
hyperbola		
latus rectum		
locus		
major axis		
minor axis		
parabola		
parameter		
parametric curve		
parametric equation		
transverse axis		
vertex (vertices)		

2

7 Anticipation Guide

Conic Sections and Parametric Equations

Step 1	**Before you begin Chapter 7**

- Read each statement.

- Decide whether you Agree (A) or Disagree (D) with the statement.

- Write A or D in the first column OR if you are not sure whether you agree or disagree, write NS (Not Sure).

STEP 1 A, D, or NS	Statement	STEP 2 A or D
	1. The graph of $y^2 = 4x$ is a parabola.	
	2. The eccentricity of an ellipse is greater than 1.	
	3. The general form of the equation of a conic section is $y = mx + b$.	
	4. There are formulas to find the coordinates of a point on the graph of a rotated conic section.	
	5. A conic section could be a triangle or a square.	
	6. The graph of a degenerate conic is a line, two intersecting lines, or a point.	
	7. The transverse axis of a hyperbola is longer than the conjugate axis.	
	8. A circle is a special type of ellipse.	

Step 2	**After you complete Chapter 7**

- Reread each statement and complete the last column by entering an A or a D.

- Did any of your opinions about the statements change from the first column?

- For those statements that you mark with a D, use a piece of paper to write an example of why you disagree.

7 Ejercicios preparatorios

Secciones cónicas y ecuaciones paramétricas

Antes de que comiences el Capítulo 7

- Lee cada enunciado.

- Decide si estás de acuerdo (A) o en desacuerdo (D) con el enunciado.

- Escribe A o D en la primera columna O si no estás seguro(a), escribe NS (no estoy seguro(a)).

PASO 1 A, D o NS	Enunciado	PASO 2 A o D
	1. La grafica de $y^2 = 4x$ es una parábola.	
	2. La excentricidad de una elipse es mayor que 1.	
	3. La forma general de la ecuación de una sección cónica es $y = mx + b$.	
	4. Existen fórmulas para calcular las coordenadas de un punto en la gráfica de una sección cónica rotada.	
	5. Una sección cónica puede ser triangular o cuadrada.	
	6. La gráfica de una cónica degenerada es una recta o un punto.	
	7. El eje transversal de una hipérbola es más largo que su eje conjugado.	
	8. Un círculo es un tipo especial de elipse.	

Después de que termines el Capítulo 7

- Relee cada enunciado y escribe A o D en la última columna.

- Compara la última columna con la primera. ¿Cambiaste de opinión sobre alguno de los enunciados?

- En los casos en que hayas estado en desacuerdo con el enunciado, escribe en una hoja aparte un ejemplo de por qué no estás de acuerdo.

7-1 Study Guide and Intervention

Parabolas

Analyze and Graph Parabolas A **parabola** is the locus of all points in a plane equidistant from a point called the **focus** and a line called the **directrix**. The standard form of the equation of a parabola that opens vertically is $(x - h)^2 = 4p(y - k)$. When p is negative, the parabola opens downward. When p is positive, it opens upward. The standard form of the equation of a parabola that opens horizontally is $(y - k)^2 = 4p(x - h)$. When p is negative, the parabola opens to the left. When p is positive, it opens to the right.

Example For $(x - 3)^2 = 12(y + 4)$, **identify the vertex, focus, axis of symmetry, and directrix. Then graph the parabola.**

The equation is in standard form and the squared term is x, which means that the parabola opens vertically. Because $4p = 12$, $p = 3$ and the graph opens upward.

The equation is in the form $(x - h)^2 = 4p(y - k)$, so $h = 3$ and $k = -4$. Use the values of h, k, and p to determine the characteristics of the parabola.

vertex:	$(3, -4)$	(h, k)	directrix:	$y = -7$	$y = k - p$
focus:	$(3, -1)$	$(h, k + p)$	axis of symmetry:	$x = 3$	$x = h$

Graph the vertex, focus, axis, and directrix of the parabola. Then make a table of values to graph the general shape of the curve.

x	y
0	$-3\frac{1}{4}$
2	$-3\frac{11}{12}$
4	$-3\frac{11}{12}$
6	$-3\frac{1}{4}$

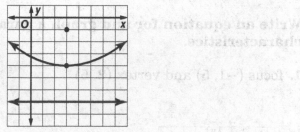

Exercises

For each equation, identify the vertex, focus, axis of symmetry, and directrix. Then graph the parabola.

1. $(y + 1)^2 = 8(x - 3)$

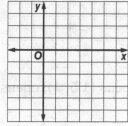

2. $(x + 2)^2 = 4(y - 1)$

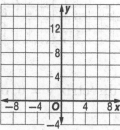

3. $(y - 3)^2 = 2(x - 6)$

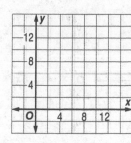

4. $\frac{1}{12}(x - 3)^2 = (y + 2)$

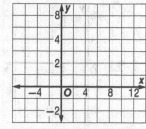

Lesson 7-1

7-1   Study Guide and Intervention *(continued)*

Parabolas

Equations of Parabolas Specific characteristics can be used to determine the equation of a parabola.

> **Example**   **Write an equation for and graph a parabola with focus $(-4, -3)$ and vertex $(1, -3)$.**
>
> Because the focus and vertex share the same y-coordinate, the graph is horizontal. The focus is $(h + p, k)$, so the value of p is $-4 - 1$ or -5. Because p is negative, the graph opens to the left.
>
> Write the equation for the parabola in standard form using the values of h, p, and k.
>
> $\begin{array}{ll} (y - k)^2 = 4p(x - h) & \text{Standard form} \\ [y - (-3)]^2 = 4(-5)(x - 1) & p = -5, h = 1, \text{ and } k = -3 \\ (y + 3)^2 = -20(x - 1) & \text{Simplify.} \end{array}$
>
> The standard form of the equation is $(y + 3)^2 = -20(x - 1)$.
>
> Graph the vertex, focus, and parabola.

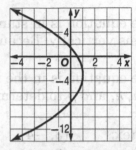

Exercises

Write an equation for and graph a parabola with the given characteristics.

1. focus $(-1, 5)$ and vertex $(2, 5)$

2. focus $(1, 4)$; opens down; contains $(-3, 1)$

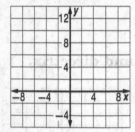

3. directrix $y = 6$; opens down; vertex $(5, 3)$

4. focus $(1.5, 1)$; opens right; directrix $x = 0.5$

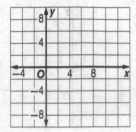
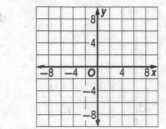

7-1   Practice

Parabolas

Identify the vertex, focus, axis of symmetry, and directrix for each equation. Then graph the parabola.

1. $(x - 1)^2 = 8(y - 2)$

2. $y^2 + 6y + 9 = 12 - 12x$

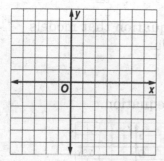

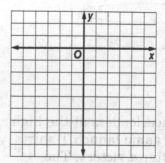

Write an equation for and graph a parabola with the given characteristics.

3. vertex $(-2, 4)$, focus $(-2, 3)$

4. focus $(2, 1)$; opens right; contains $(8, -7)$

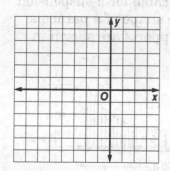

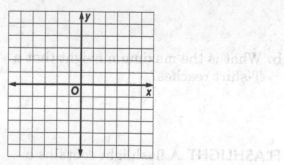

5. Write $x^2 + 8x = -4y - 8$ in standard form. Identify the vertex, focus, axis of symmetry, and directrix.

6. SATELLITE DISH Suppose the receiver in a parabolic dish antenna is 2 feet from the vertex and is located at the focus. Assume that the vertex is at the origin and that the dish is pointed upward. Find an equation that models a cross section of the dish.

7-1 Word Problem Practice

Parabolas

1. REFLECTOR The figure shows a parabolic reflecting mirror. A cross section of the mirror can be modeled by $x^2 = 16y$, where the values of x and y are measured in inches. Find the distance from the vertex to the focus of this mirror.

2. T-SHIRTS The cheerleaders at the high school basketball game launch T-shirts into the stands after a victory. The launching device propels the shirts into the air at an initial velocity of 32 feet per second. A shirt's distance y in feet above the ground after x seconds can be modeled by $y = -16x^2 + 32x + 5$.

a. Write the equation in standard form.

b. What is the maximum height that a T-shirt reaches?

3. FLASHLIGHT A flashlight contains a parabolic mirror with a bulb in the center as a light source and focus. If the width of the mirror is 4 inches at the top and the height to the focus is 0.5 inch, find an equation of the parabolic cross section.

4. ARCHWAYS The entrance to a college campus has a parabolic arch above two columns as shown in the figure.

a. Write an equation that models the parabola.

b. Graph the equation.

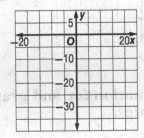

5. BRIDGES The cable for a suspension bridge is in the shape of a parabola. The vertical supports are shown in the figure.

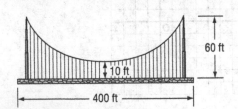

a. Write an equation for the parabolic cable.

b. Find the length of a supporting wire that is 100 feet from the center.

7-1 Enrichment

Tilted Parabolas

The diagram at the right shows a fixed point $F(1, 1)$ and a line d that has an equation $y = -x - 2$. If $P(x, y)$ satisfies the condition that $PD = PF$, then P is on a parabola. Our objective is to find an equation for the tilted parabola, which is the locus of all points that are the same distance from $(1, 1)$ and the line $y = -x - 2$.

First find an equation for the line m through $P(x, y)$ and perpendicular to line d at $D(a, b)$. Using this equation and the equation for line d, find the coordinates (a, b) of point D in terms of x and y. Then use $(PD)^2 = (PF)^2$ to find an equation for the parabola.

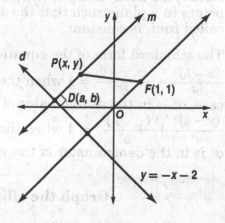

Refer to the discussion above.

1. Find an equation for line m.

2. Use the equations for lines m and d to show that the coordinates of point D are $D(a, b) = \left(\dfrac{x - y - 2}{2}, \dfrac{y - x - 2}{2} \right)$.

3. Use the coordinates of F, P, and D, along with $(PD)^2 = (PF)^2$ to find an equation of the parabola with focus F and directrix d.

4. **a.** Every parabola has an axis of symmetry. Find an equation for the axis of symmetry of the parabola described above. Justify your answer.

   b. Use your answer from part **a** to find the coordinates of the vertex of the parabola. Justify your answer.

Lesson 7-1

7-2 Study Guide and Intervention

Ellipses and Circles

Analyze and Graph Ellipses and Circles An **ellipse** is the locus of points in a plane such that the sum of the distances from two fixed points, called **foci**, is constant.

The standard form of the equation of an **ellipse** is $\frac{(x - h)^2}{a^2} + \frac{(y - k)^2}{b^2} = 1$ when the **major axis** is horizontal. In this case, a^2 is in the denominator of the x-term. The standard form is $\frac{(y - k)^2}{a^2} + \frac{(x - h)^2}{b^2} = 1$ when the major axis is vertical. In this case, a^2 is in the denominator of the y-term. In both cases, $c^2 = a^2 - b^2$.

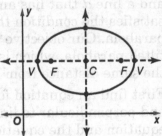

Example Graph the ellipse given by the equation $\frac{(y - 1)^2}{25} + \frac{(x + 2)^2}{9} = 1.$

The equation is in standard form. Use the values of h, k, a, and b to determine the vertices and axes of the ellipse. Since $a^2 > b^2$, $a^2 = 25$ and $b^2 = 9$, or $a = 5$ and $b = 3$. Since a^2 is the denominator of the y-term, the major axis is parallel to the y-axis.

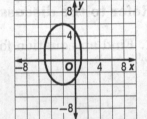

orientation:	vertical	
center:	$(-2, 1)$	(h, k)
vertices:	$(-2, 6), (-2, -4)$	$(h, k \pm a)$
co-vertices:	$(-5, 1), (1, 1)$	$(h \pm b, k)$
major axis:	$x = -2$	$x = h$
minor axis:	$y = 1$	$y = k$

Exercises

Graph the ellipse given by each equation.

1. $\frac{(x + 5)^2}{64} + \frac{(y + 2)^2}{25} = 1$

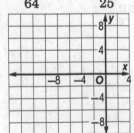

2. $\frac{(x + 2)^2}{25} + \frac{(y + 1)^2}{9} = 1$

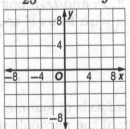

3. $\frac{(y - 1)^2}{16} + \frac{(x + 3)^2}{9} = 1$

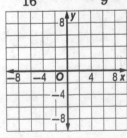

4. $\frac{(y + 3)^2}{64} + \frac{(x - 2)^2}{25} = 1$

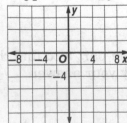

7-2 Study Guide and Intervention *(continued)*

Ellipses and Circles

Determine Types of Conic Sections If you are given the equation for a conic section, you can determine what type of conic is represented using the characteristics of the equation. The standard form of an equation for a circle with center (h, k) and radius r is $(x - h)^2 + (y - k)^2 = r^2$.

Example Write each equation in standard form. Identify the related conic.

a. $4x^2 + 9y^2 + 24x - 36y + 36 = 0$

$4x^2 + 9y^2 + 24x - 36y + 36 = 0$ Original equation

$4(x^2 + 6x + ?) + 9(y^2 - 4y + ?) = -36 + ? + ?$ Complete the square.

$4(x^2 + 6x + 9) + 9(y^2 - 4y + 4) = -36 + 36 + 36$ $\left(\frac{6}{2}\right)^2 = 9, \left(-\frac{4}{2}\right)^2 = 4$

$4(x + 3)^2 + 9(y - 2)^2 = 36$ Factor.

$\dfrac{(x + 3)^2}{9} + \dfrac{(y - 2)^2}{4} = 1$ Divide each side by 36.

Because the equation is of the form $\dfrac{(x - h)^2}{a^2} + \dfrac{(y - k)^2}{b^2} = 1$, the graph is an ellipse with center $(-3, 2)$.

b. $x^2 - 16x - 8y + 80 = 0$

$x^2 - 16x - 8y + 80 = 0$ Original equation

$(x^2 - 16x + ?) - 8y + 80 = 0$ Complete the square.

$(x^2 - 16x + 64) - 8y + 80 - 64 = 0$ $\left(\frac{16}{2}\right)^2 = 64$

$(x - 8)^2 - 8(y - 2) = 0$ Factor.

$(x - 8)^2 = 8(y - 2)$ Standard form

Because only one term is squared, the graph is a parabola with vertex $(8, 2)$.

Exercises

Write each equation in standard form. Identify the related conic.

1. $y^2 + 2y + 6x^2 - 24x = 5$ **2.** $y^2 + 2y + x^2 - 24x = 14$

3. $4x - 8 + y^2 + 4y = 0$ **4.** $x^2 + 4x + y^2 - 2y - 49 = 0$

5. $4x^2 + 8x + 5y^2 - 30y - 11 = 0$ **6.** $6x^2 + 24x + 2y - 10 = 0$

Lesson 7-2

7-2 Practice

Ellipses and Circles

Graph the ellipse given by each equation.

1. $4x^2 + 9y^2 - 8x - 36y + 4 = 0$

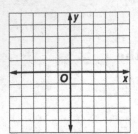

2. $25x^2 + 9y^2 - 50x - 90y + 25 = 0$

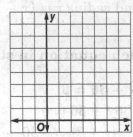

Write an equation for the ellipse with each set of characteristics.

3. vertices $(-12, 6)$, $(4, 6)$; foci $(-10, 6)$, $(2, 6)$

4. foci $(-2, 1)$, $(-2, 7)$; length of major axis 10 units

Write each equation in standard form. Identify the related conic.

5. $y^2 - 4y = 4x + 16$

6. $4x^2 - 32x + 3y^2 - 18y = -55$

7. $x^2 + y^2 - 8x - 24y = 9$

8. $x^2 + y^2 + 20x - 10y + 4 = 0$

Determine the eccentricity of the ellipse given by each equation.

9. $\dfrac{(x+1)^2}{25} + \dfrac{(y+1)^2}{16} = 1$

10. $\dfrac{(y+2)^2}{64} + \dfrac{(x+1)^2}{9} = 1$

11. CONSTRUCTION A semi-elliptical arch is used to design a headboard for a bed frame. The headboard will have a height of 2 feet at the center and a width of 5 feet at the base. Where should the craftsman place the foci in order to sketch the arch?

Glencoe Precalculus

7-2 Word Problem Practice

Ellipses and Circles

1. WHISPERING GALLERY A whispering gallery at a museum is in the shape of an ellipse. The room is 84 feet long and 46 feet wide.

a. Write an equation modeling the shape of the room. Assume that it is centered at the origin and that the major axis is horizontal.

b. Find the location of the foci.

2. SIGNS A sign is in the shape of an ellipse. The eccentricity is 0.60 and the length is 48 inches.

a. Write an equation for the ellipse if the center of the sign is at the origin and the major axis is horizontal.

b. What is the maximum height of the sign?

3. TUNNEL The entrance to a tunnel is in the shape of half an ellipse as shown in the figure.

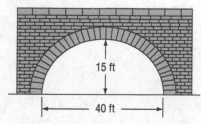

a. Write an equation that models the ellipse.

b. Find the height of the tunnel 10 feet from the center.

4. RETENTION POND A circular retention pond is getting larger by overflowing and flooding the nearby land at a rate that increases the radius 100 yards per day, as shown below.

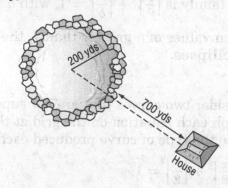

a. Graph the circle that represents the water, and find the distance from the center of the pond to the house.

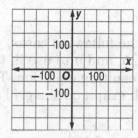

b. If the pond continues to overflow at the same rate, how many days will it take for the water to reach the house?

c. Write an equation for the circle of water at the current time and an equation for the circle when the water reaches the house.

7-2 Enrichment

Superellipses

The circle and the ellipse are members of an interesting family
of curves that were first studied by the French physicist and
mathematician Gabriel Lamé (1795-1870). The general equation
for the family is $\left|\dfrac{x}{a}\right|^n + \left|\dfrac{y}{b}\right|^n = 1$, with $a \neq 0$, $b \neq 0$, and $n > 0$.

For even values of n greater than 2, the curves are called
superellipses.

1. Consider two curves that are *not* superellipses.
   Graph each equation on the grid at the right.
   State the type of curve produced each time.

   a. $\left|\dfrac{x}{2}\right|^2 + \left|\dfrac{y}{2}\right|^2 = 1$

   b. $\left|\dfrac{x}{3}\right|^2 + \left|\dfrac{y}{2}\right|^2 = 1$

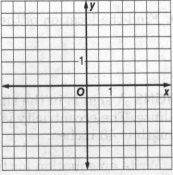

2. In each of the following cases, you are given
   values of a, b, and n to use in the general equation.
   Write the resulting equation. Then graph.
   Sketch each graph on the grid at the right.

   a. $a = 2$, $b = 3$, $n = 4$

   b. $a = 2$, $b = 3$, $n = 6$

   c. $a = 2$, $b = 3$, $n = 8$

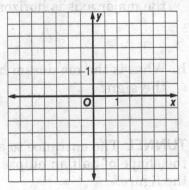

3. What shape will the graph of $\left|\dfrac{x}{2}\right|^n + \left|\dfrac{y}{3}\right|^n = 1$

   approximate for greater and greater even,
   whole-number values of n?

7-2 Graphing Calculator Activity

Translations of Ellipses

To graph an ellipse, such as $\dfrac{(x-3)^2}{18} + \dfrac{(y+2)^2}{32} = 1$, on a graphing calculator, you must first solve for y.

$$\dfrac{(x-3)^2}{18} + \dfrac{(y+2)^2}{32} = 1 \qquad \text{Original equation}$$

$$32(x-3)^2 + 18(y+2)^2 = 576 \qquad \text{Multiply each side by 576.}$$

$$18(y+2)^2 = 576 - 32(x-3)^2 \qquad \text{Subtract } 32(x-3)^2 \text{ from each side.}$$

$$(y+2)^2 = \dfrac{576 - 32(x-3)^2}{18} \qquad \text{Divide each side by 18.}$$

$$y = \pm\sqrt{\dfrac{576 - 32(x-3)^2}{18}} - 2 \qquad \text{Take the square root of each side.}$$

The result is two equations. To graph both equations in Y1, replace $\pm$ with {1, −1}. Be careful to include the proper parentheses or you will get an error message.

[Y=] [2nd] [{ }] 1 [,] [(−)] 1 [2nd] [}] [2nd] [√‾] [(] 576 [−] 32 [(] [X,T,θ,n]
[−] 3 [)] [x²] [)] [÷] 18 [)] [−] 2 [ENTER] [ZOOM] 6.

Like other graphs, there are families of ellipses. Changing certain values in the equation of an ellipse creates a new member of that family.

Exercises

Graph each equation on a graphing calculator.

1. $\dfrac{(x-7)^2}{18} + \dfrac{(y+2)^2}{32} = 1$

2. $\dfrac{(x+1)^2}{18} + \dfrac{(y+2)^2}{32} = 1$

3. $\dfrac{(x-3)^2}{18} + \dfrac{(y-2)^2}{32} = 1$

4. $\dfrac{(x-3)^2}{18} + \dfrac{(y+6)^2}{32} = 1$

5. Describe the effects of replacing $x - 3$ in Exercises 3 and 4 with $(x \pm c)$ for $c > 0$.

6. Describe the effects of replacing $y + 2$ in Exercises 1 and 2 with $(y \pm c)$ for $c > 0$.

Lesson 7-2

7-3 Study Guide and Intervention
Hyperbolas

Analyze and Graph Hyperbolas A **hyperbola** is the locus of all points in a plane such that the difference of their distances from two foci is constant. The standard form of the equation of a **hyperbola** is

$\dfrac{(x-h)^2}{a^2} - \dfrac{(y-k)^2}{b^2} = 1$ when the **transverse axis** is horizontal, and

$\dfrac{(y-k)^2}{a^2} - \dfrac{(x-h^2)}{b^2} = 1$ when the transverse axis is vertical. In both

cases, $a^2 + b^2 = c^2$.

Example Graph the hyperbola given by the equation $\dfrac{y^2}{16} - \dfrac{x^2}{4} = 1$.

The equation is in standard form. Both h and k are 0, so the center is at the origin. Because the x-term is subtracted, the transverse axis is vertical. Use the values of a, b, and c to determine the vertices and foci of the hyperbola.

Because $a^2 = 16$ and $b^2 = 4$, $a = 4$ and $b = 2$. Use the values of a and b to find the value of c.

$c^2 = a^2 + b^2$ Equation relating a, b, and c

$c^2 = 4^2 + 2^2$ a = 4 and b = 2

$c = \sqrt{20}$ or about 4.47   Simplify.

Determine the characteristics of the hyperbola.

center: $(0, 0)$ *(h, k)*   foci: $(0, \sqrt{20}), (0, -\sqrt{20})$ *(h, k ± c)*

vertices: $(0, 4), (0, -4)$ *(h, k ± a)*   asymptotes: $y = 2x, y = -2x$ $y - k = \pm\frac{a}{b}(x - h)$

Make a table of values to sketch the hyperbola.

x	y
−2	−5.65, 5.65
−1	−4.5, 4.5
0	−4, 4
1	−4.5, 4.5
2	−5.65, 5.65

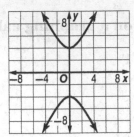

Exercises

Graph the hyperbola given by each equation.

1. $\dfrac{x^2}{25} - \dfrac{y^2}{36} = 1$

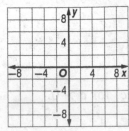

2. $\dfrac{(y-3)^2}{25} - \dfrac{(x+2)^2}{9} = 1$

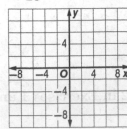

3. $\dfrac{(x-1)^2}{16} - \dfrac{(y+2)^2}{36} = 1$

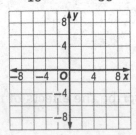

7-3 Study Guide and Intervention *(continued)*

Hyperbolas

Identify Conic Sections You can determine the type of conic when the equation for the conic is in general form, $Ax^2 + Bxy + Cy^2 + Dx + Ey + F = 0$. The discriminant, or $B^2 - 4AC$, can be used to identify a conic when the equation is in general form.

Discriminant	Conic Section
less than 0; $B = 0$ and $A = C$	circle
less than 0; $B \neq 0$ or $A \neq C$	ellipse
equal to 0	parabola
greater than 0	hyperbola

Example Use the discriminant to identify each conic section.

a. $2x^2 + 6y^2 - 8x + 12y - 2 = 0$

A is 2, B is 0, and C is 6. Find the discriminant.

$B^2 - 4AC = 0^2 - 4(2)(6)$ or -48

The discriminant is less than 0, so the conic must be either a circle or an ellipse. Because $A \neq C$, the conic is an ellipse.

b. $5x^2 + 8xy - 2y^2 + 4x - 3y + 10 = 0$

A is 5, B is 8, and C is -2. Find the discriminant.

$B^2 - 4AC = 8^2 - 4(5)(-2)$ or 104.

The discriminant is greater than 0, so the conic is a hyperbola.

c. $12x^2 + 12xy + 3y^2 - 7x + 2y - 6 = 0$

A is 12, B is 12, and C is 3. Find the discriminant.

$B^2 - 4AC = 12^2 - 4(12)(3)$ or 0

The discriminant is 0, so the conic is a parabola.

Exercises

Use the discriminant to identify each conic section.

1. $4x^2 + 4y^2 - 2x - 9y + 1 = 0$

2. $10x^2 + 6y^2 - x + 8y + 1 = 0$

3. $-2x^2 + 6xy + y^2 - 4x - 5y + 2 = 0$

4. $x^2 + 6xy + y^2 - 2x + 1 = 0$

5. $5x^2 + 2xy + 4y^2 + x + 2y + 17 = 0$

6. $x^2 + 2xy + y^2 + x + 10 = 0$

7. $25x^2 + 100x - 54y = -200$

8. $16x^2 + 100x - 54y^2 = -100$

Lesson 7-3

7-3 Practice

Hyperbolas

Graph the hyperbola given by each equation.

1. $x^2 - 4y^2 - 4x + 24y - 36 = 0$

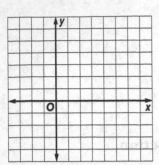

2. $\dfrac{y^2}{16} - \dfrac{(x-1)^2}{4} = 1$

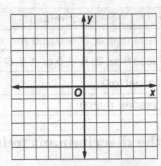

Write an equation for the hyperbola with the given characteristics.

3. vertices $(-10, 6)$, $(4, 6)$;
   foci $(-12, 6)$, $(6, 6)$

4. foci $(0, 6)$, $(0, -4)$; length of transverse axis 8 units

5. Determine the eccentricity of the hyperbola given by the equation
$\dfrac{(x-7)^2}{36} - \dfrac{(y+10)^2}{121} = 1$.

6. ENVIRONMENTAL NOISE Two neighbors who live one mile apart hear an explosion while they are talking on the telephone. One neighbor hears the explosion two seconds before the other. If sound travels at 1100 feet per second, determine the equation of the hyperbola on which the explosion was located.

Use the discriminant to identify each conic section.

7. $5x^2 + xy + 2y^2 - 5x + 8y + 9 = 0$

8. $16x^2 - 4y^2 - 8x - 8y + 1 = 0$

9. $4x^2 + 8xy + 4y^2 + x + 11y + 10 = 0$

10. $2x^2 + 4y^2 - 3x - 6y + 2 = 0$

7-3 Word Problem Practice

Hyperbolas

1. EARTHQUAKES The epicenter of an earthquake lies on a branch of the hyperbola represented by $\dfrac{(x-50)^2}{1600} - \dfrac{(y-35)^2}{2500} = 1$, where the seismographs are located at the foci.

a. Graph the hyperbola.

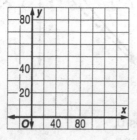

b. Find the locations of the seismographs.

2. SHADOWS A lamp projects light onto a wall in the shape of a hyperbola. The edge of the light can be modeled by $\dfrac{y^2}{196} - \dfrac{x^2}{121} = 1$.

a. Graph the hyperbola.

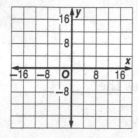

b. Write the equations of the asymptotes.

c. Find the eccentricity.

3. PARKS A grassy play area is in the shape of a hyperbola, as shown.

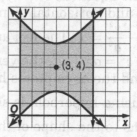

a. Write an equation that models the curved sides of the play area.

b. If each unit on the coordinate plane represents 3 feet, what is the narrowest vertical width of the play area?

4. SHADOWS The path of the shadow cast by the tip of a sundial is usually a hyperbola.

a. Write two equations of the hyperbola in standard form if the center is at the origin, given that the path contains a transverse axis of 24 millimeters with one focus 14 millimeters from the center.

b. Graph one hyperbola.

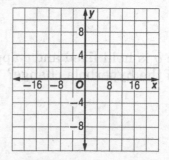

Lesson 7-3

7-3 Enrichment

Moving Foci

Recall that the equation of a hyperbola with center at the origin and horizontal transverse axis has the equation $\frac{x^2}{a^2} - \frac{y^2}{b^2} = 1$. The foci are at $(-c, 0)$ and $(c, 0)$, where $c^2 = a^2 + b^2$, the vertices are at $(-a, 0)$ and $(a, 0)$, and the asymptotes have equations $y = \pm \frac{b}{a} x$. Such a hyperbola is shown at the right.

What happens to the shape of the graph as c grows very large or very small?

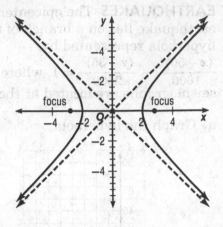

Refer to the hyperbola described above.

1. Write a convincing argument to show that as c approaches 0, the foci, the vertices, and the center of the hyperbola become the same point.

2. Use a graphing calculator or computer to graph $x^2 - y^2 = 1$, $x^2 - y^2 = 0.1$, and $x^2 - y^2 = 0.01$. (Such hyperbolas correspond to smaller and smaller values of c.) Describe the changes in the graphs. What shape do the graphs approach as c approaches 0?

3. Suppose a is held fixed and c approaches infinity. How does the graph of the hyperbola change?

4. Suppose b is held fixed and c approaches infinity. How does the graph of the hyperbola change?

7-4 Study Guide and Intervention

Rotations of Conic Sections

Rotation of Conic Sections An equation $Ax^2 + Bxy + Cy^2 + Dx + Ey + F = 0$ in the xy-plane can be rewritten as $A(x')^2 + C(y')^2 + Dx' + Ey' + F = 0$ in the $x'y'$-plane by rotating the coordinate axes through an angle θ. The equation in the $x'y'$-plane can be found using $x = x' \cos \theta - y' \sin \theta$ and $y = x' \sin \theta + y' \cos \theta$.

Example Use $\theta = 45°$ to write the standard form of $x^2 - 2xy - 4y^2 + \dfrac{1}{2} = 0$ in the $x'y'$-plane. Then identify the conic.

The conic is a hyperbola because $B^2 - 4AC > 0$. Find the equations for x and y.

$x = x' \cos \theta - y' \sin \theta$ Rotation equations for x and y $y = x' \sin \theta + y' \cos \theta$

$= \dfrac{\sqrt{2}}{2} x' - \dfrac{\sqrt{2}}{2} y'$ $\sin \dfrac{\pi}{4} = \dfrac{\sqrt{2}}{2}$ and $\cos \dfrac{\pi}{4} = \dfrac{\sqrt{2}}{2}$ $= \dfrac{\sqrt{2}}{2} x' + \dfrac{\sqrt{2}}{2} y'$

Substitute into the original equation.

$$x^2 \qquad\qquad - 2xy \qquad\qquad - 4y^2 \qquad\qquad + \frac{1}{2} = 0$$

$$\left(\frac{\sqrt{2}x' - \sqrt{2}\,y'}{2} \right)^2 - 2\left(\frac{\sqrt{2}x' - \sqrt{2}y'}{2} \right)\left(\frac{\sqrt{2}x' + \sqrt{2}y'}{2} \right) - 4\left(\frac{\sqrt{2}x' + \sqrt{2}y'}{2} \right)^2 + \frac{1}{2} = 0 \qquad \text{Replace } x \text{ and } y.$$

$$\frac{1}{2}(x')^2 - x'y' + \frac{1}{2}(y')^2 - (x')^2 + (y')^2 - 2(x')^2 - 4x'y' - 2(y')^2 + \frac{1}{2} = 0 \qquad \text{Expand the binomials.}$$

$$-\frac{5}{2}(x')^2 - 5x'y' - \frac{1}{2}(y')^2 + \frac{1}{2} = 0 \qquad \text{Simplify.}$$

The equation of the hyperbola after the 45° rotation is $5(x')^2 + 10x'y' + (y')^2 = 1$.

Exercises

Write each equation in the $x'y'$-plane for the given value of θ. Then identify the conic.

1. $x^2 - 4x + y^2 = 2$, $\theta = \dfrac{\pi}{4}$ **2.** $8x^2 - 5y^2 = 40$, $\theta = 30°$

Lesson 7-4

7-4 Study Guide and Intervention (continued)

Rotations of Conic Sections

Graph Rotated Conics When the equations of rotated conics are given for the $x'y'$-plane, they can be graphed by finding points on the graph of the conic and then converting these points to the xy-plane.

Example Graph $\dfrac{(x')^2}{36} + \dfrac{(y')^2}{64} = 1$ if it has been rotated 30° from its position in the xy-plane.

The equation represents an ellipse, and it is in standard form. Use the center $(0, 0)$; the vertices $(0, 8)$, $(0, -8)$; and the co-vertices $(6, 0)$, $(-6, 0)$ to determine the center and vertices for the ellipse in the xy-plane.

Find the equations for x and y for $\theta = 30°$.

$$x = x' \cos \theta - y' \sin \theta \qquad \text{Rotation equations for } x \text{ and } y \qquad y = x' \sin \theta + y' \cos \theta$$

$$= \frac{\sqrt{3}}{2} x' - \frac{1}{2} y' \qquad \sin 30° = \frac{1}{2} \text{ and } \cos 30° = \frac{\sqrt{3}}{2} \qquad = \frac{1}{2} x' + \frac{\sqrt{3}}{2} y'$$

Use the equations to convert the $x'y'$-coordinates of the center into xy-coordinates.

$$x = \frac{\sqrt{3}}{2}(0) - \frac{1}{2}(0) \qquad x' = 0 \text{ and } y' = 0 \qquad y = \frac{1}{2}(0) + \frac{\sqrt{3}}{2}(0)$$

$$= 0 \qquad \text{Multiply.} \qquad = 0$$

Likewise, convert the coordinates of the vertices and co-vertices into xy-coordinates.

$$(0, 8) \to (-4, 4\sqrt{3}) \quad (0, -8) \to (4, -4\sqrt{3}) \quad (6, 0) \to (3\sqrt{3}, 3) \quad (-6, 0) \to (-3\sqrt{3}, -3)$$

The new center, vertices, and co-vertices can be used to sketch the graph of the ellipse in the xy-plane.

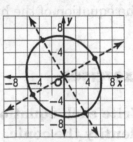

Exercises

Graph each equation at the indicated angle.

1. $(x' + 6)^2 = 12(y' + 2); \dfrac{\pi}{2}$

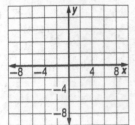

2. $\dfrac{(x')^2}{9} - \dfrac{(y')^2}{4} = 1; 60°$

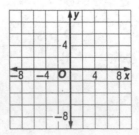

7-4 Practice

Rotations of Conic Sections

Write each equation in the $x'y'$-plane for the given value of θ. Then identify the conic.

1. $xy = 1$; $\theta = \dfrac{\pi}{4}$

2. $5x^2 + 6y^2 = 30$; $\theta = 30°$

Write an equation for each conic in the xy-plane for the given equation in $x'y'$ form and the given value of θ.

3. $(x')^2 = 16(y')$; $\theta = 45°$

4. $\dfrac{(x')^2}{25} - \dfrac{(y')^2}{4} = 1$; $\theta = \dfrac{\pi}{3}$

Determine the angle θ through which the conic with each equation should be rotated. Then write the equation in standard form.

5. $x^2 + xy + y^2 = 2$

6. $13x^2 - 8xy + 7y^2 - 45 = 0$

7. $16x^2 - 24xy + 9y^2 - 30x - 40y = 0$

8. $18x^2 + 12xy + 13y^2 - 198 = 0$

9. COMMUNICATIONS Suppose the orientation of a satellite dish that monitors radio waves is modeled by the equation $4x^2 + 2xy + 4y^2 + \sqrt{2}x - \sqrt{2}y = 0$. What is the angle of rotation of the satellite dish about the origin?

10. Graph $(x' + 1)^2 = -16(y' + 3)$ if it has been rotated 45° from its position in the xy-plane.

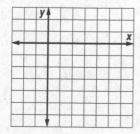

Lesson 7-4

7-4 Word Problem Practice

Rotations of Conic Sections

1. **COMMUNICATIONS** A satellite dish is modeled by the equation $y = \frac{1}{8}x^2$ when it is directly overhead. Later in the day, the dish has rotated 60°.

   a. Write an equation that models the new orientation of the satellite dish.

   b. Draw the graph.

   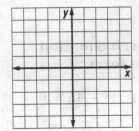

2. **GEARS** Suppose the equation of an elliptical gear rotated 60° in the $x'y'$-plane is $\frac{(x')^2}{16} + \frac{(y')^2}{20} = 1$.

   a. Write an equation for the ellipse formed by the gear in the xy-plane.

   b. Draw the graph.

   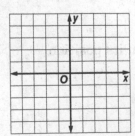

3. **ART** Mimi is drawing a picture with rotated parabolas. She wants to graph $(x' - 3)^2 = 12(y' - 4)$ if it has been rotated 45° from the xy-plane.

   a. Find the vertex in the xy-plane.

   b. Find the equation for the axis of symmetry in the xy-plane.

   c. Draw the graph in the xy-plane.

   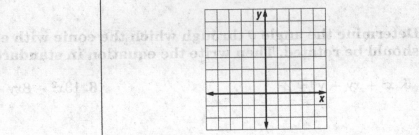

4. **LOGIC** A hyperbola has been rotated 40° clockwise. Through what angle must it be rotated to return it to its original position?

5. **SHAPES** The shape of a reflecting mirror in a telescope can be modeled by $25x^2 + 13xy + 2y^2 = 100$. Determine whether the reflector is elliptical, parabolic, or hyperbolic.

7-4 Enrichment

Graphing with Addition of y-Coordinates

Equations of parabolas, ellipses, and hyperbolas that are "tipped" with respect to the x- and y-axes are more difficult to graph than the equations you have been studying.

Often, however, you can use the graphs of two simpler equations to graph a more complicated equation. For example, the graph of the ellipse in the diagram at the right is obtained by adding the y-coordinate of each point on the circle and the y-coordinate of the corresponding point of the line.

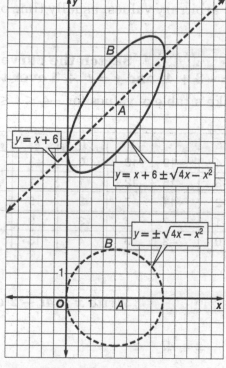

$y = x + 6$

$y = x + 6 \pm \sqrt{4x - x^2}$

$y = \pm\sqrt{4x - x^2}$

Graph each equation. State the type of curve for each graph.

1. $y = 6 - x \pm \sqrt{4 - x^2}$

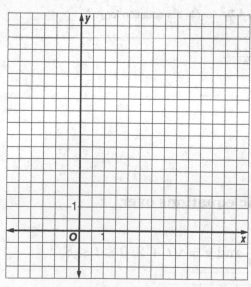

2. $y = x \pm \sqrt{x}$

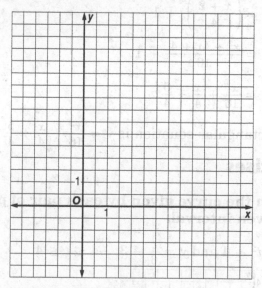

Use a separate sheet of graph paper to graph these equations. State the type of curve for each graph.

3. $y = 2x \pm \sqrt{7 + 6x - x^2}$

4. $y = -2x \pm \sqrt{-2x}$

Lesson 7-4

7-5 Study Guide and Intervention

Parametric Equations

Graph Parametric Equations **Parametric equations** are used to describe the horizontal and vertical components of an equation. **Parameters** are arbitrary values, usually time or angle measurement.

Example 1 Sketch the curve given by the parametric equations $x = -3 + 4t$ and $y = t^2 + 3$ over the interval $-4 \le t \le 4$.

Make a table of values for $-4 \le t \le 4$.

t	x	y	t	x	y
−4	−19	19	0	−3	3
−3	−15	12	1	1	4
−2	−11	7	2	5	7
−1	−7	4	3	9	12
0	−3	3	4	13	19

Plot the (x, y) coordinates for each t-value and connect the points to form a smooth curve.

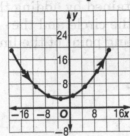

Example 2 Write $x = 4t - 2$ and $y = t^2 + 1$ in rectangular form.

$$x = 4t - 2$$ Parametric equation for x

$$\frac{x + 2}{4} = t$$ Solve for t.

$$y = \left(\frac{x + 2}{4}\right)^2 + 1$$ Substitute $\frac{x+2}{4}$ for t in the equation for y.

$$= \frac{x^2 + 4x + 4}{16} + 1$$ Square $\frac{x+2}{4}$.

$$= \frac{x^2}{16} + \frac{x}{4} + \frac{5}{4}$$ Simplify.

The rectangular equation is $y = \frac{x^2}{16} + \frac{x}{4} + \frac{5}{4}$.

Exercises

Sketch the curve given by each pair of parametric equations over the given interval.

1. $x = t^2 + 4$ and $y = \frac{t}{6} - 3$; $-4 \le t \le 4$

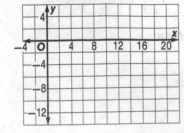

2. $x = \frac{t}{3}$ and $y = \sqrt{t} + 2$; $0 \le t \le 8$

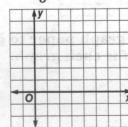

7-5 Study Guide and Intervention *(continued)*

Parametric Equations

Projectile Motion Parametric equations are often used to simulate projectile motion. For an object launched at an angle θ with the horizontal at an initial velocity v_0, where g is the gravitational constant, t is time, and h_0 is the initial height, the horizontal distance x can be found by $x = tv_0 \cos \theta$ and the vertical position y by $y = tv_0 \sin \theta - \frac{1}{2}gt^2 + h_0$.

Example Luigi is kicking a soccer ball. He kicks the ball with an initial velocity of 35 feet per second at an angle of 48° with the horizontal. The ball is 2 feet above the ground when he kicks it. How far will the ball travel horizontally before it hits the ground?

Step 1 Make a diagram of the situation.

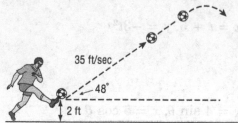

35 ft/sec
48°
2 ft

Step 2 Write a parametric equation for the vertical position of the ball.

$y = tv_0 \sin \theta - \frac{1}{2}gt^2 + h_0$ Parametric equation for vertical position

$= t(35) \sin (48) - \frac{1}{2}(32)t^2 + 2$ $v_0 = 35, \theta = 48°, g = 32,$ and $h_0 = 2$

Step 3 Graph the equation for the vertical position and the line $y = 0$. Use **5: INTERSECT** on the **CALC** menu of a calculator to find the point of intersection of the curve with $y = 0$. The value is about 1.7 seconds. You could also use **2: ZERO** and not graph $y = 0$.

Step 4 Determine the horizontal position of the ball at 1.7 seconds.

$x = tv_0 \cos \theta$ Parametric equation for horizontal position

$= 1.7(35) \cos 48$ $v_0 = 35, \theta = 48°,$ and $t = 1.7$

≈ 39.8 Use a calculator.

The ball will travel about 39.8 feet before it hits the ground.

Exercises

1. Julie is throwing a ball at an initial velocity of 28 feet per second and an angle of 56° with the horizontal from a height of 4 feet. How far away will the ball land?

2. Jerome hits a tennis ball at an initial velocity of 38 feet per second and an angle of 42° with the horizontal from a height of 1.5 feet. How far away will the ball land if it is not hit by his opponent?

Lesson 7-5

7-5 Practice

Parametric Equations

Sketch the curve given by each pair of parametric equations over the given interval.

1. $x = t^2 + 1$ and $y = \dfrac{t}{2} - 6;\ -5 \le t \le 5$

2. $x = 2t + 6$ and $y = -\dfrac{t^2}{2};\ -5 \le t \le 5$

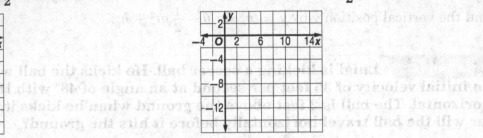

Write each pair of parametric equations in rectangular form.

3. $x = 2t + 3,\ y = t - 4$

4. $x = t + 5,\ y = -3t^2$

5. $x = 3 \sin \theta,\ y = 2 \cos \theta$

6. $y = 4 \sin \theta,\ x = 5 \cos \theta$

Use each parameter to write the parametric equations that can represent each equation. Then graph the equation, indicating the speed and orientation.

7. $t = \dfrac{2 - x}{3}$ for $y = \dfrac{3 - x^2}{2}$

8. $t = 4x - 1$ for $y = x^2 + 2$

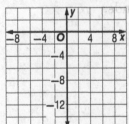

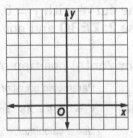

9. MODEL ROCKETRY Manuel launches a toy rocket from ground level with an initial velocity of 80 feet per second at an angle of 80° with the horizontal.

   a. Write parametric equations to represent the path of the rocket.

   b. How long will it take the rocket to travel 10 feet horizontally from its starting point? What will be its vertical distance at that point?

7-5 Word Problem Practice

Parametric Equations

1. **PHYSICS** A rock is thrown at an initial velocity of 5 meters per second at an angle of 8° with the ground. After 0.4 second, how far has the rock traveled horizontally?

2. **PLAYING CATCH** Tom and Sarah are playing catch. Tom tosses a ball to Sarah at an initial velocity of 38 feet per second at an angle of 28° from a height of 4 feet. Sarah is 40 feet away from Tom.

   a. How high above the ground will the ball be when it gets to Sarah?

   b. What is the maximum height of the ball?

3. **TENNIS** Melinda hits a tennis ball with an initial velocity of 42 feet per second at an angle of 16° with the horizontal from a height of 2 feet. She is 20 feet from the net and the net is 3 feet high. Will the ball go over the net?

4. **BASKETBALL** Mandy throws a basketball with an initial velocity of 28 feet per second at an angle of 60° with the horizontal. If Mandy releases the ball from a height of 5 feet, write a pair of equations to determine the vertical and horizontal positions of the ball.

5. **GOLF** Julio hit a golf ball with an initial velocity of 100 feet per second at an angle of 39° with the horizontal.

   a. Write parametric equations for the flight of the ball.

   b. Find the maximum height the ball reaches.

6. **BASEBALL** Micah hit a baseball at an initial velocity of 120 feet per second from a height of 3 feet at an angle of 34°.

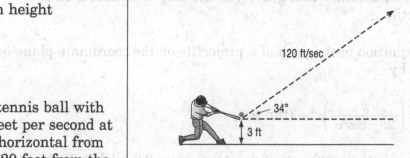

   a. How far will the ball travel horizontally before it hits the ground?

   b. What is the maximum height the ball will reach?

   c. If the fence is 8 feet tall and 400 feet from home plate, will the ball clear the fence to be a home run? Explain.

7-5 Enrichment

Coordinate Equations of Projectiles

The path of a projectile after it is launched is a parabola when graphed
on a coordinate plane.

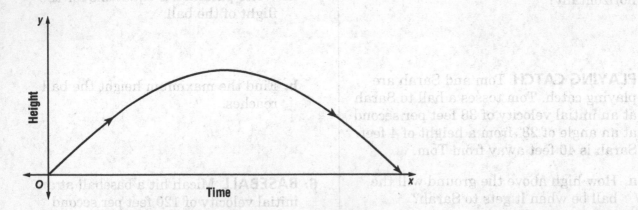

The path assumes that gravity is the only force acting on the
projectile.

The equation of the path of a projectile on the coordinate plane is
given by

$$y = -\left(\frac{g}{2v_0^2 \cos^2\alpha}\right)x^2 + (\tan \alpha)x,$$

where g is the acceleration due to gravity, 9.8 m/s^2 or 32 ft/s^2,
v_0 is the initial velocity, and α is the angle at which the
projectile is fired.

Example Write the equation of a projectile fired at an angle of
10° to the horizontal with an initial velocity of 120 m/s.

$$y = -\left(\frac{9.8}{2(120)^2 \cos^2 10°}\right)x^2 + (\tan 10°)x$$

$$y = -0.00035x^2 + 0.18x$$

Find the equation of the path of each projectile.

1. a projectile fired at 80° to the
   horizontal with an initial velocity
   of 200 ft/s

2. a projectile fired at 40° to the
   horizontal with an initial velocity
   of 150 m/s

7-5 Spreadsheet Activity

Parametric Equations

You have learned that the motion of orbiting planets can be modeled using parametric equations. A spreadsheet can be used to evaluate parametric equations and to provide a graph of a planet's orbit.

	A	B	C
1	t	x	y
2	2	8.676882	3.855863
3	4	6.356741	7.045013
4	6	2.935661	9.016016
5	8	−0.99302	9.428068
6	10	−4.75	8.209921

Use the parametric equations for Saturn's position in its orbit in a spreadsheet. To calculate the x position, enter the following formula in B2: = 9.5*COS(PI()15*A2). To calculate the y position, enter the formula = 9.48*SIN(PI()15*A2) in C2. Use the fill handle to paste these formulas into the remaining cells in columns B and C.

In the spreadsheet, the values in column A represent t, and the values in columns B and C represent the calculated x and y values of Saturn's position at time t.

Exercises

1. Complete the spreadsheet to find the position of Saturn every 2 years from t = 2 to t = 32. Use the spreadsheet to make an X-Y graph of Saturn's position.

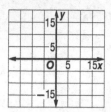

2. Find the coordinates representing Saturn's position after 23 years.

3. Given the parametric equations $x = 6 \sin 3t$ and $y = -4 \cos t$, write the formulas to put into your spreadsheet if time is found in cell A2.

Lesson 7-5

7 Chapter 7 Quiz 1

(Lessons 7-1 and 7-2)

SCORE _____

1. Write $16x^2 + 4y^2 - 96x + 8y + 84 = 0$ in standard form. Identify the related conic.

1. _____

2. Graph the ellipse given by $\dfrac{(x-6)^2}{64} + \dfrac{(y+1)^2}{100} = 1$.

2.

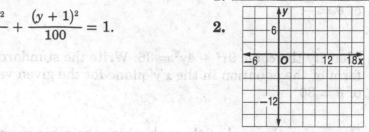

3. Identify the vertex, focus, axis of symmetry, and directrix for $x^2 - 4x + 8y + 12 = 0$.

3. _____

4. Write an equation for the ellipse with vertices $(-8, 5)$, $(4, 5)$ and foci $(-7, 5)$, $(3, 5)$.

4. _____

5. **MULTIPLE CHOICE** Write an equation for the parabola with vertex $(0, 0)$ and directrix $x = -8$.

    A $y^2 = -32x$ **B** $y^2 = -16x$ **C** $y^2 = -8x$ **D** $y^2 = 32x$

5. _____

- -

7 Chapter 7 Quiz 2

(Lesson 7-3)

SCORE _____

1. Graph the hyperbola given by $\dfrac{(y-2)^2}{4} - \dfrac{(x+5)^2}{9} = 1$.

1.

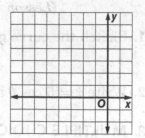

2. Write an equation for the hyperbola with vertices $(-4, -1)$, $(2, -1)$ and foci $(-5, -1)$, $(3, -1)$.

2. _____

3. Find the eccentricity of the ellipse given by $\dfrac{(x+3)^2}{49} + \dfrac{(y-6)^2}{121} = 1$.

3. _____

4. Use the discriminant to identify the conic given by $24x^2 - 4y^2 - 150x - 16y = -109$.

4. _____

5. **MULTIPLE CHOICE** Write an equation for the hyperbola with vertices $(0, -6)$, $(0, 6)$ and foci $(0, -9)$, $(0, 9)$.

    A $\dfrac{y^2}{36} + \dfrac{x^2}{45} = 1$ **C** $\dfrac{x^2}{36} - \dfrac{y^2}{45} = 1$

    B $\dfrac{y^2}{45} - \dfrac{x^2}{36} = 1$ **D** $\dfrac{y^2}{36} - \dfrac{x^2}{45} = 1$

5. _____

7 Chapter 7 Quiz 3

(Lesson 7-4)

SCORE _____

1. Identify the conic $x^2 + xy - y^2 = 6$. Write the equation in the $x'y'$-plane for the given value of $\theta = \frac{\pi}{4}$.

1. _____

2. Identify the conic $9x^2 + 4y^2 = 36$. Write the standard form of the equation in the $x'y'$-plane for the given value of $\theta = 30°$.

2. _____

3. Determine the angle θ through which the conic given by $8x^2 + 8xy - 7y^2 = 15$ should be rotated.

3. _____

4. Write an equation in the xy-plane for the conic given by $\frac{(x')^2}{36} - \frac{(y')^2}{9} = 1$ in $x'y'$ form and for $\theta = 60°$.

4. _____

5. **MULTIPLE CHOICE** Identify the conic $xy = -8$.

   A circle   C ellipse

   B parabola   D hyperbola

5. _____

---

7 Chapter 7 Quiz 4

(Lesson 7-5)

SCORE _____

1. Sketch the curve given by $x = -3t^2$ and $y = 2t$, $-2 \le t \le 2$.

1.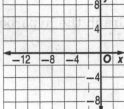

2. Write $x = 5 \cos \theta$ and $y = 7 \sin \theta$ in rectangular form.

3. **MULTIPLE CHOICE** Rewrite $y = t^2 + 4$ and $x = 2t - 5$ in rectangular form.

   A $y = (x + 5)^2$

   B $y = \dfrac{(x + 5)^2}{4}$

   C $y = 4x^2 - 20x + 29$

   D $y - 4 = \dfrac{(x + 5)^2}{4}$

2. _____

3. _____

While positioned 25 yards directly in front of the goalposts, Bill kicks the football with an initial velocity of 65 feet per second at an angle of 35° with the ground.

4. Write the position of the football as a pair of parametric equations. If the crossbar is 10 feet above the ground, does Bill's team score?

4. _____

5. What is the elapsed time from the moment the football is kicked to the time the ball hits the ground?

5. _____

7 Chapter 7 Mid-Chapter Test

SCORE _____

(Lessons 7-1 through 7-3)

Part I Write the letter for the correct answer in the blank at the right of each question.

1. Which is the graph of $(y - 6)^2 = 4(x - 2)$?

A 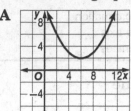 B 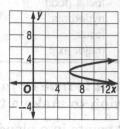 C 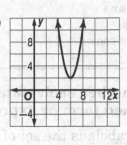 D

1. _____

2. Which is the equation for an ellipse with vertices $(-3, 4)$, $(11, 4)$ and foci $(-1, 4)$, $(9, 4)$?

F $\dfrac{(x - 4)^2}{49} + \dfrac{(y - 4)^2}{24} = 1$

H $\dfrac{x^2}{7} + \dfrac{y^2}{5} = 1$

G $\dfrac{(x - 4)^2}{49} + \dfrac{(y - 4)^2}{25} = 1$

J $\dfrac{(x - 4)^2}{24} - \dfrac{(y - 4)^2}{49} = 1$

2. _____

3. Which are the equations of the asymptotes of $\dfrac{x^2}{36} - \dfrac{y^2}{25} = 1$?

A $y = \pm \dfrac{6}{5} x$

C $y = \pm \dfrac{36}{25} x$

B $y = \pm \dfrac{5}{6} x$

D $y = \pm \dfrac{25}{36} x$

3. _____

4. Use the discriminant to identify the conic given by $4x^2 + 10x + 2y + 8 = 0$.

F ellipse   **G** hyperbola   **H** parabola   **J** circle

4. _____

Part II

5. Write an equation for the hyperbola with vertices $(2, 5)$, $(2, -3)$ and conjugate axis of length 10.

5. _____

6. The entrance to a zoo is in the shape of a parabola. Write an equation for the parabola if the origin is at the vertex.

6. _____

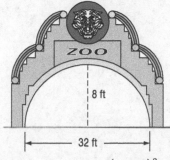

7. Graph the hyperbola given by $\dfrac{(y - 6)^2}{9} - \dfrac{(x + 1)^2}{4} = 1$.

7.

7 Chapter 7 Vocabulary Test

axis of symmetry	eccentricity	minor axis
conic section	ellipse	parabola
conjugate axis	focus (foci)	parameter
co-vertices	hyperbola	parametric equation
degenerate conic	locus	transverse axis
directrix	major axis	vertex (vertices)

State whether each statement is *true* or *false*. If false, replace the underlined term or expression to make a true sentence.

1. A <u>parabola</u> is the set of all points in a plane equidistant from a point and a line in the same plane.

1. _____

2. In an ellipse, the relationship between the values a, b, and c is given by the equation $a^2 + b^2 = c^2$.

2. _____

3. The length of the major $\overline{\text{axis of}}$ an ellipse is <u>greater than</u> the length of the minor axis.

3. _____

4. The eccentricity of a hyperbola is <u>less than</u> one.

4. _____

5. The foci of a hyperbola are on the <u>conjugate axis</u>.

5. _____

6. The intersection of a double-napped right cone and a plane is a <u>conic section</u>.

6. _____

7. The axis of symmetry of a parabola is a line through the focus, <u>parallel</u> to the directrix.

7. _____

8. The equation of a line tangent to a parabola can be found using an <u>isosceles triangle</u>.

8. _____

9. The slopes of the asymptotes of a vertical hyperbola are $\pm \dfrac{b}{a}$.

9. _____

Define each term in your own words.

10. hyperbola

11. degenerate conic

7   Chapter 7 Test, Form 1   SCORE _____

Write the letter for the correct answer in the blank at the right of each question.

For Questions 1–3, refer to the ellipse represented by $\dfrac{(x-1)^2}{16} + \dfrac{(y+2)^2}{9} = 1.$

1. Find the coordinates of the center.

   A $(1, 2)$ **B** $(1, -2)$ **C** $(-1, 2)$ **D** $(-2, 1)$ **1.** _____

2. Find the coordinates of the foci.

   F $\left(1 \pm \sqrt{7}, -2\right)$ **H** $(5, -2), (-3, -2)$

   G $\left(1, -2 \pm \sqrt{7}\right)$ **J** $(1, 4), (1, -8)$ **2.** _____

3. Find the coordinates of the vertices and co-vertices.

   A $(1, 2), (1, -6), (4, -2), (-2, -2)$ **C** $(5, -2), (-3, -2), (1, 1), (1, -5)$

   B $(4, 2), (-2, 2), (1, 1), (1, -5)$ **D** $(5, -2), (-3, -2), (1, 2), (1, -6)$ **3.** _____

4. Determine the angle of rotation θ through which the conic given by $4x^2 - 4xy + y^2 = 4$ should be rotated.

   F $27°$ **G** $63°$ **H** $117°$ **J** $153°$ **4.** _____

5. Write the pair of parametric equations $x = 5 \cos \theta$ and $y = -\sin \theta$ in rectangular form.

   A $\dfrac{x^2}{5} + y^2 = 1$ **B** $\dfrac{x^2}{5} - y^2 = 1$ **C** $\dfrac{x^2}{25} + y^2 = 1$ **D** $\dfrac{x^2}{25} - y^2 = 1$ **5.** _____

6. Use the discriminant to identify the conic section $9y^2 + 4x^2 - 108y + 24x = -144.$

   F parabola   **G** hyperbola   **H** ellipse   **J** circle   **6.** _____

7. Write the standard form of the equation $y^2 - x^2 = 5$ in the $x'y'$-plane after a rotation of $45°$.

   A $x'y' = 2.5$ **C** $(y')^2 - (x')^2 = 2.5$

   B $x'y' = -5$ **D** $(x')^2 = 2.5y'$ **7.** _____

8. Marcy hit a golf ball with initial velocity of 130 feet per second at an angle of $28°$ with the ground. Write parametric equations to represent this situation.

   F $x = 130t \cos 28°$ **H** $x = 28t \cos 130°$

      $y = 130t \sin 28° - 16t^2$ $y = 28t \sin 130° - 16t^2$

   G $x = 130t \cos 28° - 16t^2$ **J** $x = 28 \cos 130t°$

      $y = 130t \cos 28°$ $y = 28 \cos 130t°$ **8.** _____

9. A cross section of the reflector shown is in the shape of a parabola. Which of the following is an equation for the cross section?

   A $y^2 = 4x$ **C** $x^2 = 4y$

   B $y^2 = 8x$ **D** $x^2 = 8y$ **9.** _____

(diagram labeled 4 in. and 2 in.)

Assessment

For Questions 10 and 11, refer to the hyperbola represented by $\frac{y^2}{4} - \frac{x^2}{2} = 1$.

10. Write the equations of the asymptotes.

   F $y = \pm 2x$ **G** $y = \pm \frac{1}{2}x$ **H** $y = \pm \sqrt{2}x$ **J** $y = \pm \frac{\sqrt{2}}{2}x$ 10. _____

11. Find the coordinates of the foci.

   A $(0, \pm\sqrt{2})$ **B** $(0, \pm\sqrt{6})$ **C** $(\pm\sqrt{2}, 0)$ **D** $(\pm\sqrt{6}, 0)$ 11. _____

12. Write the standard form of the equation of the hyperbola for which the transverse axis is 4 units long and vertical and the conjugate axis is 3 units long.

   F $\dfrac{(x-1)^2}{2.25} - \dfrac{(y+4)^2}{4} = 1$ **H** $\dfrac{(y+4)^2}{2.25} - \dfrac{(x-1)^2}{4} = 1$

   G $\dfrac{(y+4)^2}{4} - \dfrac{(x-1)^2}{2.25} = 1$ **J** $\dfrac{(x-1)^2}{4} - \dfrac{(y+4)^2}{2.25} = 1$ 12. _____

13. Darius serves a volleyball with an initial velocity of 34 feet per second 4 feet above the ground at an angle of 35°. What is the maximum height, reached after about 0.61 second?

   A 2.14 ft   **B** 9.94 ft   **C** 5.94 ft   **D** 6.14 ft   13. _____

14. Write the standard form of the equation of the parabola with directrix at $x = -1$ and with focus at $(5, -2)$.

   F $(y+2)^2 = 12(x+2)$ **H** $(y+2)^2 = 12(x+2)$

   G $y - 2 = 12(x+2)^2$ **J** $(y+2)^2 = 12(x-2)$ 14. _____

15. Identify the graph of the equation $16x^2 - 24xy + 9y^2 - 30x - 40y = 0$.

   A hyperbola   **B** ellipse   **C** parabola   **D** circle   15. _____

16. Which graph represents a curve with parametric equations $x = t - 4$ and $y = t^2$ over the interval $-2 \leq t \leq 2$?

   F 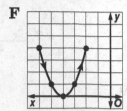   **G** 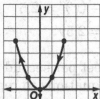   **H** 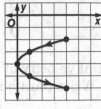   **J** 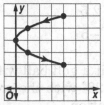   16. _____

17. Identify the conic that may have an eccentricity of $\frac{4}{3}$.

   A circle   **B** ellipse   **C** hyperbola   **D** parabola   17. _____

18. Write the standard form of the equation of the circle with center at $(2, -7)$ and radius 5.

   F $(x-2)^2 + (y+7)^2 = 25$ **H** $(x-2)^2 + (y+7)^2 = 16$

   G $(x-2)^2 + (y+7)^2 = 5$ **J** $(x+2)^2 + (y-7)^2 = 25$ 18. _____

Bonus   Write the equation of the line tangent to $y = x^2$ at $(2, 4)$.   B: _____

7 | Chapter 7 Test, Form 2A

SCORE _____

Write the letter for the correct answer in the blank at the right of each question.

For Questions 1–3, refer to the ellipse represented by the equation
$\frac{(x-3)^2}{25} + (y-2)^2 = 1.$

1. Find the coordinates of the center.

   A $(2, 3)$ **B** $(3, 2)$ **C** $(-3, -2)$ **D** $(-2, -3)$ **1.** _____

2. Find the coordinates of the foci.

   F $\left(3, 2 \pm 2\sqrt{6}\right)$ **G** $(-2, 2), (8, 2)$ **H** $\left(3 \pm 2\sqrt{6}, 2\right)$ **J** $\left(2 \pm 2\sqrt{6}, 3\right)$ **2.** _____

3. Find the coordinates of the vertices and co-vertices.

   A $(8, 2), (-2, 2), (3, 3), (3, 1)$ **C** $(4, 2), (2, 2), (3, 3), (3, 1)$

   B $(8, 2), (-2, 2), (3, 7), (3, -3)$ **D** $(4, 2), (2, 2), (3, 7), (3, -3)$ **3.** _____

4. Determine the angle of rotation θ through which the conic
   given by equation $2x^2 + 3xy + y^2 = 1$ should be rotated.

   F $-9°$ **G** $36°$ **H** $-36°$ **J** $324°$ **4.** _____

5. Write the pair of parametric equations $x = 3 \cos \theta$ and $y = \sin \theta$
   in rectangular form.

   A $\frac{x^2}{9} + y^2 = 1$ **B** $\frac{x^2}{9} - y^2 = 1$ **C** $y^2 - \frac{x^2}{3} = 1$ **D** $y^2 + \frac{x^2}{3} = 1$ **5.** _____

6. Use the discriminant to identify the conic section
   $3y^2 - 3x^2 + 12y + 18x = 42.$

   F parabola   **G** hyperbola   **H** ellipse   **J** circle   **6.** _____

7. Write the standard form of the equation $y^2 - x^2 = 2$ in the $x'y'$ plane
   after a rotation of $45°$.

   A $x'y' = 1$ **B** $x'y' = -2$ **C** $(y')^2 - (x')^2 = 2$ **D** $(x')^2 = y'$ **7.** _____

8. Randall hit a golf ball with initial velocity of 120 feet per second at
   an angle of $38°$ with the ground. Write parametric equations
   to represent this situation.

   F $x = 120t \cos 38° - 16t^2$
         $y = 120t \sin 38°$
                   H $x = 38t \cos 120°$
                    $y = 38t \sin 120° - 16t^2$

   G $x = 120t \cos 38°$
         $y = 120t \sin 38° - 16t^2$
                J $x = 38 \cos 120t°$
                  $y = 38 \cos 120t°$ **8.** _____

9. A cross section of the reflector shown is in the
   shape of a parabola. Write an equation for the
   cross section.

   A $y^2 = 4x$ **C** $x^2 = 4y$

   B $y^2 = 8x$ **D** $x^2 = 8y$ **9.** _____

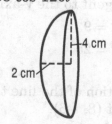

4 cm

2 cm

Assessment

For Questions 10 and 11, refer to the hyperbola represented by $\dfrac{(y+2)^2}{36} - x^2 = 1$.

10. Write the equations of the asymptotes.

   F $y - 1 = \pm 6(x - 2)$ **H** $y + 2 = \pm 6(x - 1)$

   G $y = \pm 6x$ **J** $y + 2 = \pm 6x$ **10.** _____

11. Find the coordinates of the foci.

   A $\left(1 \pm \sqrt{37}, -2\right)$ **B** $\left(\pm\sqrt{37}, -2\right)$ **C** $\left(6 \pm \sqrt{37}, -2\right)$ **D** $\left(0, -2 \pm \sqrt{37}\right)$ **11.** _____

12. Write the standard form of the equation of the hyperbola for which $a = 2$, the transverse axis is vertical, and the equations of the asymptotes are $y = \pm 2x$.

   F $\dfrac{x^2}{4} - y^2 = 1$ **G** $y^2 - \dfrac{x^2}{4} = 1$ **H** $x^2 - \dfrac{y^2}{4} = 1$ **J** $\dfrac{y^2}{4} - x^2 = 1$ **12.** _____

13. Aaron kicked a soccer ball with an initial velocity of 39 feet per second at an angle of 44° with the horizontal. After 0.9 second, how far has the ball traveled horizontally?

   A 24.4 ft   **B** 12.3 ft   **C** 11.4 ft   **D** 25.2 ft   **13.** _____

14. Write the standard form of the equation of the parabola with directrix at $y = -4$ and focus at $(2, 2)$.

   F $(y - 2)^2 = 12(x + 2)$ **H** $(x + 2)^2 = 12(y - 2)$

   G $y + 1 = 12(x - 2)^2$ **J** $(x - 2)^2 = 12(y + 1)$ **14.** _____

15. Identify the graph of the equation $4x^2 - 5xy + 16y^2 - 32 = 0$.

   A circle   **B** ellipse   **C** parabola   **D** hyperbola   **15.** _____

16. Which graph represents a curve given by $x = 4t + 5$ and $y = 2t^2$ over the interval $-3 \le t \le 3$?   **16.** _____

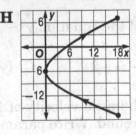
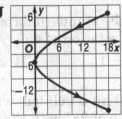

17. Identify the conic that has an eccentricity of $\dfrac{2}{3}$.

   A circle   **B** ellipse   **C** hyperbola   **D** parabola   **17.** _____

18. Write the standard form of the equation of the circle with center at $(-3, 5)$ that is tangent to the y-axis.

   F $(x + 3)^2 + (y - 5)^2 = 9$ **H** $(x + 3)^2 + (y - 5)^2 = 3$

   G $(x + 3)^2 + (y - 5)^2 = 25$ **J** $(x - 3)^2 + (y + 5)^2 = 9$ **18.** _____

Bonus Write the equation of the line tangent to $(y - 2)^2 = 8x$ at $(8, -6)$.   **B:** _____

7 Chapter 7 Test, Form 2B

SCORE _____

Write the letter for the correct answer in the blank at the right of each question.

For Questions 1–3, refer to the ellipse represented by $\dfrac{x^2}{9} + \dfrac{(y-1)^2}{4} = 1.$

1. Find the coordinates of the center.

  A $(-1, 0)$ **B** $(0, -1)$ **C** $(1, 0)$ **D** $(0,1)$ **1.** _____

2. Find the coordinates of the foci.

  F $\left(0, 1 \pm \sqrt{5}\right)$ **H** $\left(\sqrt{5}, 3\right), \left(-\sqrt{5}, 3\right)$

  G $\left(\sqrt{5}, 1\right), \left(-\sqrt{5}, 1\right)$ **J** $(1, 5), (1, -5)$ **2.** _____

3. Find the coordinates of the vertices and co-vertices.

  A $(2, 1), (-2, 1), (0, 4), (0, -2)$ **C** $(3, 1), (-3, 1), (0, 4), (0, -2)$

  B $(3, 1), (-3, 1), (0, 3), (0, -1)$ **D** $(2, 1), (-2, 1), (0, 3), (0, -1)$ **3.** _____

4. Determine the angle of rotation θ through which the conic given by $2x^2 + xy + 2y^2 = 1$ should be rotated.

  F $215°$ **G** $150°$ **H** $45°$ **J** $-30°$ **4.** _____

5. Write the pair of parametric equations $x = -\cos\theta$ and $y = \sin\theta$ in rectangular form.

  A $y^2 - x^2 = 1$ **B** $x^2 + y^2 = -1$ **C** $x^2 + y^2 = 1$ **D** $x^2 - y^2 = 1$ **5.** _____

6. Use the discriminant to identify the conic section $x^2 - y^2 + 12y + 18x = 42.$

  F parabola   **G** hyperbola   **H** ellipse   **J** circle   **6.** _____

7. Write the standard form of the equation $x^2 + y^2 = 16$ in the $x'y'$-plane after a rotation of $45°$.

  A $(x')^2 + (y')^2 = 16$ **C** $(x')^2 - 2x'y' + (y')^2 = 16$

  B $(x')^2 - (y')^2 = 16$ **D** $(x')^2 + 2x'y' + (y')^2 = 16$ **7.** _____

8. Rusty hit a baseball with initial velocity of 125 feet per second at an angle of 32° with the ground from a height of 3 feet. Write parametric equations to represent this situation.

  F $x = 125t \cos 32° - 16t^2$

       $y = 125t \sin 32° + 3$

  G $x = 32 \cos 125t° + 3$

       $y = 32 \cos 125t°$

  H $x = 32t \cos 125°$

       $y = 32t \sin 125° - 16t^2$

  J $x = 125t \cos 32°$

       $y = 125t \sin 32° - 16t^2 + 3$ **8.** _____

9. A cross section of the reflector shown is in the shape of a parabola. Write an equation for the cross section.

  A $y^2 = 12x$ **C** $x^2 = 4y$

  B $y^2 = 8x$ **D** $x^2 = 8y$ **9.** _____

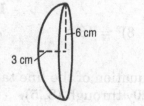

6 cm

3 cm

Assessment

For Questions 10 and 11, refer to the hyperbola represented by $\dfrac{(x-3)^2}{16} - \dfrac{y^2}{9} = 1$.

10. Write the equations of the asymptotes.

F $y - 3 = \pm\frac{4}{3}x$ **G** $y - 3 = \pm\frac{3}{4}x$ **H** $y = \pm\frac{4}{3}(x - 3)$ **J** $y = \pm\frac{3}{4}(x - 3)$ **10.** _____

11. Find the coordinates of the foci.

A $(5, 0), (-5, 0)$ **B** $(0, 5), (0, -5)$ **C** $(3, 5), (3, -5)$ **D** $(8, 0), (-2, 0)$ **11.** _____

12. Write the standard form of the equation of the hyperbola for which $a = 5$, $b = 6$, the transverse axis is vertical, and the center is at the origin.

F $\dfrac{y^2}{25} - \dfrac{x^2}{36} = 1$ **G** $\dfrac{x^2}{36} - \dfrac{y^2}{25} = 1$ **H** $\dfrac{x^2}{25} - \dfrac{y^2}{36} = 1$ **J** $\dfrac{y^2}{36} - \dfrac{x^2}{25} = 1$ **12.** _____

13. Jana hit a golf ball with an initial velocity of 102 feet per second at an angle of 67° with the horizontal. After 2 seconds, how far has the ball traveled horizontally?

A 27.9 ft   **B** 123.8 ft   **C** 79.7 ft   **D** 97.7 ft   **13.** _____

14. Write the standard form of the equation of the parabola with directrix at $x = -2$ and focus at $(2, 0)$.

F $(y - 2)^2 = 8(x - 2)$ **H** $y^2 = 8x$

G $(y - 2)^2 = 4(x - 2)$ **J** $x^2 = 8y$ **14.** _____

15. Identify the graph of $6x^2 - 8xy - 2y^2 + 6 = 0$.

A circle   **B** ellipse   **C** hyperbola   **D** parabola   **15.** _____

16. Which graph represents a curve given by $x = t - 2$ and $y = t^2 - 2$ over the interval $-3 \le t \le 3$?

F 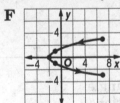   **G** 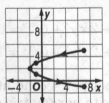   **H** 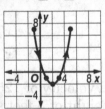   **J** 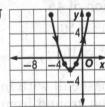   **16.** _____

17. Identify the conic with an eccentricity of 1.

A circle   **B** ellipse   **C** hyperbola   **D** parabola   **17.** _____

18. Write the standard form of the equation of the circle with center at $(-4, 8)$ that is tangent to the x-axis.

F $x^2 + y^2 = 64$ **H** $(x - 4)^2 + (y + 8)^2 = 16$

G $(x + 4)^2 + (y - 8)^2 = 16$ **J** $(x + 4)^2 + (y - 8)^2 = 64$ **18.** _____

Bonus Write the equation of the line tangent to $(x + 2)^2 = 20y$ through $(8, 5)$.   **B:** _____

7   Chapter 7 Test, Form 2C

SCORE _____

For Questions 1–3, use the ellipse represented by $3x^2 + 2y^2 + 24x - 4y + 26 = 0$.

1. Find the center.

1. _____

2. Find the foci.

2. _____

3. Find the vertices and co-vertices.

3. _____

4. Determine the angle of rotation θ through which the conic given by $4x^2 + 12xy - 5y^2 = -3$ should be rotated, to the nearest degree.

4. _____

5. Write the pair of parametric equations $x = 8 \cos \theta$ and $y = -2 \sin \theta$ in rectangular form.

5. _____

6. Use the parameter $t = 2x - 3$ to determine the parametric equations that can represent $y = x^2 + 1$.

6. _____

7. Write the standard form of $x^2 - xy + y^2 = \dfrac{3}{2}$ in the $x'y'$-plane after a rotation of 45° about the origin.

7. _____

8. Tomas hit a baseball with an initial velocity of 100 feet per second at an angle of 35° with the ground from a height of 4 feet. Write parametric equations to represent this situation.

8. _____

9. The figure shows a parabolic archway. Write an equation for the parabola.

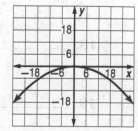

9. _____

For Questions 10 and 11, use the hyperbola given by $\dfrac{(y - 6)^2}{64} - \dfrac{(x - 9)^2}{81} = 1$.

10. Find the foci.

10. _____

11. Find the equations of the asymptotes.

11. _____

12. Write the standard form equation of the hyperbola with foci at $(-2, -3 \pm 2\sqrt{3})$ and conjugate axis of length 6 units.

12. _____

13. Find the coordinates of the vertex and the equation of the axis of symmetry for the parabola represented by $x = y^2 - 2y - 5$.

13. _____

14. Write the standard form equation of the parabola with a vertex at $(-2, 1)$, and focus at $(-2, -4)$.

14. _____

15. Use the discriminant to identify the conic given by $xy + 3y + 4x = 0$.

15. _____

16. Graph the curve given by the parametric equations $x = 2t + 3$ and $y = t^2 - 1$ over the interval $-3 \le t \le 3$.

16.

For Questions 17 and 18, Lisset throws a softball from a height of 4 feet with an initial velocity of 60 feet per second at an angle of 45° with respect to the horizontal.

17. When will the ball be a horizontal distance of 30 feet from Lisset?

17. _____

18. What is the maximum height the ball will reach?

18. _____

19. Identify the conic section with eccentricity $\frac{9}{5}$.

19. _____

20. Write the equation of a circle with center $(2, 7)$ and diameter 30.

20. _____

Bonus Write a rectangular equation for the curve given by $x = 3\cos(4\theta) + 2$ and $y = 2\sin(4\theta) - 5$.

B: _____

7　Chapter 7 Test, Form 2D

SCORE _____

For Questions 1–3, use the ellipse represented by $4x^2 + 9y^2 - 24x + 18y + 9 = 0$.

1. Find the center.

1. _____

2. Find the foci.

2. _____

3. Find the vertices and co-vertices.

3. _____

4. Determine the angle of rotation θ through which the conic given by $3x^2 - 8xy - 3y^2 = 3$ should be rotated, to the nearest degree.

4. _____

5. Write the parametric equations $x = 10 \cos \theta$ and $y = 3 \sin \theta$ in rectangular form.

5. _____

6. Use the parameter $t = 2x + 4$ to determine the parametric equations that can represent $y = x^2 + 2$.

6. _____

7. Write the standard form of $5x^2 + 3\sqrt{3}\,xy + 2y^2 = 13$ in the $x'y'$-plane after a rotation of 30° about the origin.

7. _____

8. Lucinda hit a softball with an initial velocity of 110 feet per second at an angle of 32° with the ground from a height of 3 feet. Write parametric equations to represent this situation.

8. _____

9. The figure shows a parabolic archway. Write an equation for the parabola.

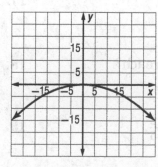

9. _____

For Questions 10 and 11, use the hyperbola given by $4x^2 - y^2 + 24x + 4y + 28 = 0$.

10. Find the foci.

10. _____

11. Find the equations of the asymptotes.

11. _____

NAME ________________________ DATE ____________ PERIOD ____________

7 Chapter 7 Test, Form 2D *(continued)*

12. Write the standard form equation of the hyperbola with foci at $(-1, -2 \pm 2\sqrt{5})$ and conjugate axis of length 8 units. **12.** ____________

13. Find the coordinates of the vertex and the equation of the axis of symmetry for the parabola represented by $-2x + y^2 - 2y + 5 = 0$. **13.** ____________

14. Write the equation in standard form of the parabola with vertex $(2, -5)$, directrix $y = -1$, and opens down. **14.** ____________

15. Use the discriminant to identify the conic given by $4x^2 + 8xy - 2y^2 = 17$. **15.** ____________

16. Graph the curve given by the parametric equations $x = 2t + 5$ and $y = t^2 - 2$ over the interval $-3 \le t \le 3$. **16.**

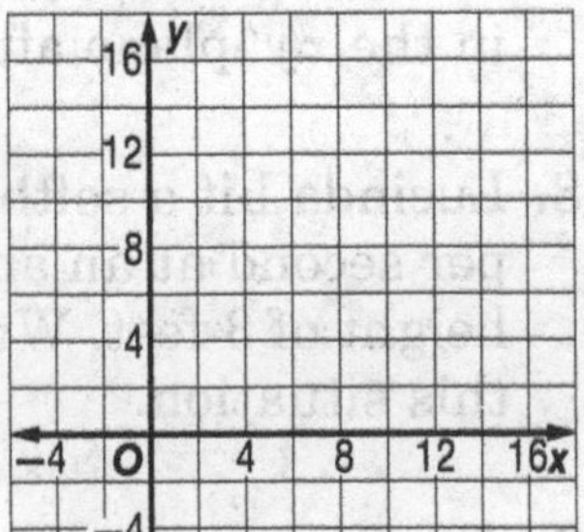

For Questions 17 and 18, Alfie throws a softball from a height of 5 feet with an initial velocity of 65 feet per second at an angle of 42° with respect to the horizontal.

17. When will the ball be a horizontal distance of 30 feet from Alfie? **17.** ____________

18. What is the maximum height the ball will reach? **18.** ____________

19. Identify the conic section with eccentricity $\frac{2}{5}$. **19.** ____________

20. Write the equation of a circle with center $(-6, -9)$ and diameter 22. **20.** ____________

Bonus Write a rectangular equation for the curve given by $x = 5 \cos(3\theta) - 4$ and $y = 2 \sin(3\theta) + 1$. **B:** ____________

7 **Chapter 7 Test, Form 3** SCORE _____

For Questions 1–3, use the ellipse represented by $9x^2 + 4y^2 + 54x - 16y + 61 = 0$.

1. Find the center.

1. _____

2. Find the foci.

2. _____

3. Find the vertices and co-vertices.

3. _____

4. Identify the graph of $14x^2 - 7xy - 10y^2 = 5$. Find θ, the angle of rotation about the origin, to the nearest degree.

4. _____

5. Write the parametric equations $x = 2 \cos 3\theta$ and $y = -3 \sin 3\theta$ in rectangular form.

5. _____

6. Use the parameter $t = 3x - 2$ to determine the parametric equations that can represent $y = -x^2 + 4$.

6. _____

7. Write the standard form of $5x^2 - \sqrt{3}xy + 4y^2 = 20$ in the $x'y'$-plane after a rotation of 60° about the origin.

7. _____

8. Jim threw a ball with an initial velocity of 38 feet per second at an angle of 29° from a height of 4 feet to Jennifer, who was standing 42 feet away. Jim's dog Rex was between them, 4 feet in front of Jennifer. If Rex can jump 5 feet into the air, can Rex intercept the ball? Write the parametric equations for the flight of the ball and explain your answer.

8. _____

9. The figure shows the entrance to a tunnel in the shape of a parabola. Write an equation for the parabola.

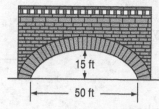

9. _____

For Questions 10 and 11, use the hyperbola represented by $y^2 + 4y - 4x^2 - 8x + 16 = 0$.

10. Find the foci.

10. _____

11. Find the equations of the asymptotes.

11. _____

12. Write the equation in standard form of the hyperbola with a horizontal transverse axis of length 10, center at $(-2, 4)$, and asymptotes $y - 4 = \pm\frac{4}{5}(x + 2)$.

12.

13. Find the coordinates of the vertex and the equation of the axis of symmetry for the parabola represented by $y^2 + 4y - 4x + 12 = 0$.

13.

14. Write the standard form equation of the parabola that passes through the point $(-8, 15)$, has vertex at $(2, -5)$, and opens to the left.

14.

15. Use the discriminant to identify the conic given by $xy = 36$.   15.

16. Graph the curve given by parametric equations $x = -\frac{1}{2}t^2$ and $y = \frac{t}{4} - 3$ over the interval $-4 \leq t \leq 4$.

16.

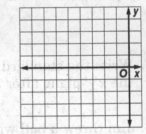

For Questions 17 and 18, Shannon kicks a soccer ball with an initial velocity of 45 feet per second at an angle of 12° with respect to the horizontal.

17. After 0.5 second, what is the height of the ball?   17.

18. The goal is 4 feet high and 20 feet in front of Shannon. Will the ball go into the goal before it hits the ground, assuming she kicks it straight ahead of her and the goalkeeper does not stop it? Explain.

18.

19. Find the eccentricity of the conic represented by $\frac{(x - 2)^2}{4} + \frac{(y + 3)^2}{8} = 1$.

19.

20. Write the equation of a circle with a diameter whose endpoints are $(-4, 6)$ and $(30, 18)$.

20.

Bonus   Find the equation of the ellipse with a center at $(-1, 3)$, a vertical minor axis of length 40 units, and eccentricity of $\frac{3}{5}$.

B:

7 Extended-Response Test

SCORE _____

Demonstrate your knowledge by giving a clear, concise solution to each problem. Be sure to include all relevant drawings and justify your answers. You may show your solution in more than one way or investigate beyond the requirements of the problem.

1. Consider the equation of a conic section written in the form
$Ax^2 + By^2 + Cx + Dy + E = 0$.

  a. Explain how you can tell if the equation is that of a circle. Write an equation of a circle with a center not at the origin. Graph the equation.

  b. Explain how you can tell if the equation is that of an ellipse. Write an equation of an ellipse with a center not at the origin. Graph the equation.

  c. Explain how you can tell if the equation is that of a parabola. Write an equation of a parabola with its vertex at $(-1, 2)$. Graph the equation.

  d. Explain how you can tell if the equation is that of a hyperbola. Write an equation of a hyperbola with a vertical transverse axis.

  e. Identify the graph of $3x^2 - xy + 2y^2 - 3 = 0$. Then find the angle of rotation θ to the nearest degree.

2. a. Describe the graph of $x^2 - 4y^2 = 0$.

  b. Graph the relation to verify your conjecture.

  c. What conic section does this graph represent?

3. Give a real-world example of a conic section. Discuss how you know the object is a conic section and analyze the conic section if possible.

Assessment

7 Standardized Test Practice

(Chapters 1–7)

Part 1: Multiple Choice
Instructions: Fill in the appropriate circle for the best answer.

1. Find the remainder when $5x^3 + 8x - 2$ is divided by $x - 3$.

A -161 **B** 19 **C** 67 **D** 157 **1.** Ⓐ Ⓑ Ⓒ Ⓓ

2. Find the period and phase shift of the graph of $f(x) = -4\cos 2(x + \pi)$.

F $2, 4$ right **G** $\pi, 2\pi$ left **H** π, π left **J** $2\pi, \pi$ right **2.** Ⓕ Ⓖ Ⓗ Ⓙ

3. Solve $2\cos^2 x + 5\cos x - 3 = 0$ where $0 \le x < 2\pi$.

A $\dfrac{\pi}{3}, \dfrac{5\pi}{3}$ **B** $\dfrac{\pi}{3}, \dfrac{2\pi}{3}$ **C** $\dfrac{\pi}{6}, \dfrac{5\pi}{6}$ **D** $\dfrac{\pi}{6}, \dfrac{11\pi}{6}$ **3.** Ⓐ Ⓑ Ⓒ Ⓓ

4. Find $\cos\dfrac{7\pi}{12}$.

F $\dfrac{1 + \sqrt{2}}{2}$ **G** $\dfrac{1}{4}$ **H** $\dfrac{\sqrt{2} - \sqrt{6}}{4}$ **J** $\dfrac{\sqrt{2} + \sqrt{6}}{4}$ **4.** Ⓕ Ⓖ Ⓗ Ⓙ

5. Write the expression for the numerator of x for this system of equations using Cramer's Rule.
$$2x - 5y + z = 6$$
$$-3x + 4y - 2z = -9$$
$$x + 2y + 4z = 5$$

A $\begin{vmatrix} 2 & 5 & 6 \\ -3 & 4 & -9 \\ 1 & 2 & 5 \end{vmatrix}$ **B** $\begin{vmatrix} 2 & -5 & 1 \\ -3 & 4 & -2 \\ 1 & 2 & 4 \end{vmatrix}$ **C** $\begin{vmatrix} 6 & -5 & 1 \\ -9 & 4 & -2 \\ 5 & 2 & 4 \end{vmatrix}$ **D** $\begin{vmatrix} 2 & 6 & 1 \\ -3 & -9 & -2 \\ 1 & 5 & 4 \end{vmatrix}$ **5.** Ⓐ Ⓑ Ⓒ Ⓓ

6. Find $\sin\dfrac{7\pi}{6}$.

F $-\dfrac{\sqrt{3}}{2}$ **G** $-\dfrac{1}{2}$ **H** $\dfrac{1}{2}$ **J** $\dfrac{\sqrt{3}}{2}$ **6.** Ⓕ Ⓖ Ⓗ Ⓙ

7. Find $\sin\left(\arccos -\dfrac{5}{7}\right)$.

A $-\dfrac{2}{7}$ **B** $\dfrac{25}{49}$ **C** $-\dfrac{\sqrt{24}}{7}$ **D** $\dfrac{2\sqrt{6}}{7}$ **7.** Ⓐ Ⓑ Ⓒ Ⓓ

8. Find $f^{-1}(x)$ if $f(x) = 2x - 6$.

F $f^{-1}(x) = \dfrac{x + 6}{2}$ **H** $f^{-1}(x) = \dfrac{1}{2x - 6}$

G $f^{-1}(x) = -2x + 6$ **J** $f^{-1}(x) = \dfrac{1}{2}x + 6$ **8.** Ⓕ Ⓖ Ⓗ Ⓙ

7 Standardized Test Practice (continued)
(*Chapters 1–7*)

9. Find the equation of the horizontal asymptote of $g(x) = \dfrac{2x - 10}{x + 3}$.

A $y = 5$ **B** $y = -3$ **C** $y = 2$ **D** $y = -\dfrac{10}{3}$ **9.** Ⓐ Ⓑ Ⓒ Ⓓ

10. The graph of $g(x) = (x - 2)^3 + 3$ can be obtained from the graph of $f(x) = x^3$ by doing which transformation?

F move right 2 and up 3 **H** move left 2 and up 3
G move right 2 and down 3 **J** move left 2 and down 3 **10.** Ⓕ Ⓖ Ⓗ Ⓙ

11. If $f(x) = -2x^3$, where is $f(x)$ decreasing?

A $(-\infty, \infty)$ **C** $(0, \infty)$
B $(-\infty, 0)$ **D** $(-10, 10)$ **11.** Ⓐ Ⓑ Ⓒ Ⓓ

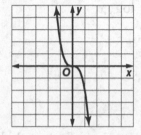

12. Find the eccentricity of the conic represented by
$\dfrac{(x - 6)^2}{100} + \dfrac{(y - 4)^2}{144} = 1$.

F $\dfrac{5}{6}$ **G** $\dfrac{6}{5}$ **H** $\dfrac{\sqrt{11}}{6}$ **J** $\dfrac{\sqrt{11}}{5}$ **12.** Ⓕ Ⓖ Ⓗ Ⓙ

13. Find the value of $\begin{vmatrix} 2 & 3 & 0 \\ -1 & 4 & -2 \\ 5 & 0 & -3 \end{vmatrix}$.

A -49 **B** -63 **C** -67 **D** -79 **13.** Ⓐ Ⓑ Ⓒ Ⓓ

14. Change $105°$ to radians.

F $\dfrac{5\pi}{12}$ **G** $\dfrac{7\pi}{12}$ **H** $\dfrac{3\pi}{4}$ **J** $\dfrac{5\pi}{6}$ **14.** Ⓕ Ⓖ Ⓗ Ⓙ

15. If $\cos x = -\dfrac{7}{25}$ and $\pi < x < \dfrac{3\pi}{2}$, find $\sin 2x$.

A $\dfrac{336}{625}$ **B** $-\dfrac{336}{625}$ **C** $-\dfrac{48}{25}$ **D** $-\dfrac{527}{625}$ **15.** Ⓐ Ⓑ Ⓒ Ⓓ

16. Find the domain of $f(x) = \dfrac{x + 2}{3x - 1}$.

F $\{x \mid x \in \mathbb{R}\}$ **H** $\{x \mid x \neq -2, x \in \mathbb{R}\}$
G $\left\{x \mid x \neq \dfrac{1}{3}, x \in \mathbb{R}\right\}$ **J** $\left\{x \mid x \neq -2, \dfrac{1}{3}, x \in \mathbb{R}\right\}$ **16.** Ⓕ Ⓖ Ⓗ Ⓙ

17. If $f(x) = 2x + 7$ and $g(x) = x^2 - 3$, find $f(g(x))$.

A $2x^3 + 7x^2 - 6x - 21$ **C** $4x^2 + 28x + 46$
B $x^2 + 2x + 4$ **D** $2x^2 + 1$ **17.** Ⓐ Ⓑ Ⓒ Ⓓ

18. Find the element in row 2, column 1 of the product $\begin{bmatrix} 2 & -6 \\ 5 & 9 \end{bmatrix} \cdot \begin{bmatrix} 1 & -1 \\ 4 & -2 \end{bmatrix}$.

F -24 **G** 19 **H** 36 **J** 41 **18.** Ⓕ Ⓖ Ⓗ Ⓙ

19. Find $\log_2 32$.

A 2 **B** 5 **C** 16 **D** 64 **19.** Ⓐ Ⓑ Ⓒ Ⓓ

Assessment

7 Standardized Test Practice (continued)

(Chapters 1–7)

Part 2: Short Response
Instructions: Write your answers in the space provided.

20. Find a rectangular form of an equation given by $x = 10 \cos \theta$ and $y = 4 \sin \theta$.

20. _____

21. Graph $y = \log_2 x$.

21.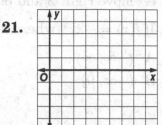

22. Write an equation of a parabola with vertex $(4, 9)$ and focus $(4, 11)$.

22. _____

23. Determine the angle θ through which the conic given by $4x^2 + 4xy + y^2 + x - 2y = 13$ should be rotated. Then write the equation in standard form.

23. _____

24. Find the coordinates of the center of the conic represented by $4x^2 - 8x + 5y^2 + 40y = 16$.

24. _____

25. Roads from town C to town A and town B form an angle of $100°$ as shown in the figure. Find the distance from A to B to the nearest tenth of a mile.

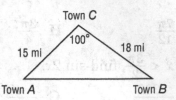

25. _____

26. Write $\ln 6$ in terms of base 4 logarithms.

26. _____

27. Solve $(x - 3)(x + 4)(x - 1) > 0$.

27. _____

28. Ned hit a baseball with an initial velocity of 85 feet per second at a height of 3 feet and an angle of $34°$ with the horizontal.

   a. Write parametric equations to represent the flight of the baseball.

28a. _____

   b. Find the maximum height the ball reaches.

28b. _____

   c. Find the horizontal distance the ball travels before it hits the ground.

28c. _____

Answers (Anticipation Guide and Lesson 7-1)

NAME _____ DATE _____ PERIOD _____

7-1 Study Guide and Intervention

Parabolas

Analyze and Graph Parabolas A parabola is the locus of all points in a plane equidistant from a point called the **focus** and a line called the **directrix**. The standard form of the equation of a parabola that opens vertically is $(x - h)^2 = 4p(y - k)$. When p is positive, the parabola opens upward. When p is negative, the parabola opens downward. The standard form of the equation of a parabola that opens horizontally is $(y - k)^2 = 4p(x - h)$. When p is positive, the parabola opens to the right. When p is negative, the parabola opens to the left.

Example For $(x - 3)^2 = 12(y + 4)$, identify the vertex, focus, axis of symmetry, and directrix. Then graph the parabola.

The equation is in standard form and the squared term is x, which means that the parabola opens vertically. Because $4p = 12$, $p = 3$ and the graph opens upward.

The equation is in the form $(x - h)^2 = 4p(y - k)$, so $h = 3$ and $k = -4$. Use the values of h, k, and p to determine the characteristics of the parabola.

vertex: $(3, -4)$ (h, k) directrix: $y = -7$ $y = k - p$
focus: $(3, -1)$ $(h, k + p)$ axis of symmetry: $x = 3$ $x = h$

Graph the vertex, focus, axis, and directrix of the parabola. Then make a table of values to graph the general shape of the curve.

x	y
0	$-3\frac{1}{4}$
2	$-3\frac{11}{12}$
4	$-3\frac{11}{12}$
6	$-3\frac{1}{4}$

Exercises

For each equation, identify the vertex, focus, axis of symmetry, and directrix. Then graph the parabola.

1. $(y + 1)^2 = 8(x - 3)$

$(3, -1)$; $(5, -1)$;
$y = -1$; $x = 1$

2. $(x + 2)^2 = 4(y - 1)$

$(-2, 1)$; $(-2, 2)$;
$x = -2$; $y = 0$

3. $(y - 3)^2 = 2(x - 6)$

$(6, 3)$; $(6\frac{1}{2}, 3)$;
$y = 3$; $x = 5\frac{1}{2}$

4. $\frac{1}{12}(x - 3)^2 = (y + 2)$

$(3, -2)$; $(3, 1)$;
$x = 3$; $y = -5$

NAME _____ DATE _____ PERIOD _____

7 Anticipation Guide

Conic Sections and Parametric Equations

Step 1 *Before you begin Chapter 7*

- Read each statement.
- Decide whether you Agree (A) or Disagree (D) with the statement.
- Write A or D in the first column OR if you are not sure whether you agree or disagree, write NS (Not Sure).

STEP 1 A, D, or NS	Statement	STEP 2 A or D
	1. The graph of $y^2 = 4x$ is a parabola.	A
	2. The eccentricity of an ellipse is greater than 1.	D
	3. The general form of the equation of a conic section is $y = mx + b$.	D
	4. There are formulas to find the coordinates of a point on the graph of a rotated conic section.	A
	5. A conic section could be a triangle or a square.	D
	6. The graph of a degenerate conic is a line, two intersecting lines, or a point.	A
	7. The transverse axis of a hyperbola is longer than the conjugate axis.	D
	8. A circle is a special type of ellipse.	A

Step 2 *After you complete Chapter 7*

- Reread each statement and complete the last column by entering an A or a D.
- Did any of your opinions about the statements change from the first column?
- For those statements that you mark with a D, use a piece of paper to write an example of why you disagree.

Answers

NAME _____ DATE _____ PERIOD _____

7-1 Practice

Parabolas

Identify the vertex, focus, axis of symmetry, and directrix for each equation. Then graph the parabola.

1. $(x - 1)^2 = 8(y - 2)$

vertex: $(1, 2)$; focus: $(1, 4)$;
axis of symmetry: $x = 1$;
directrix: $y = 0$

2. $y^2 + 6y + 9 = 12 - 12x$

vertex: $(1, -3)$; focus: $(-2, -3)$;
axis of symmetry: $y = -3$;
directrix: $x = 4$

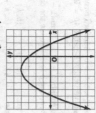

Write an equation for and graph a parabola with the given characteristics.

3. vertex $(-2, 4)$, focus $(-2, 3)$

$(x + 2)^2 = -4(y - 4)$

4. focus $(2, 1)$; opens right; contains $(8, -7)$

$(y - 1)^2 = 8x$

5. Write $x^2 + 8x = -4y - 8$ in standard form. Identify the vertex, focus, axis of symmetry, and directrix.

$(x + 4)^2 = -4(y - 2)$; $(-4, 2)$; $(-4, 1)$; $x = -4$; $y = 3$

6. **SATELLITE DISH** Suppose the receiver in a parabolic dish antenna is 2 feet from the vertex and is located at the focus. Assume that the vertex is at the origin and that the dish is pointed upward. Find an equation that models a cross section of the dish.

$x^2 = 8y$

NAME _____ DATE _____ PERIOD _____

7-1 Study Guide and Intervention *(continued)*

Parabolas

Equations of Parabolas Specific characteristics can be used to determine the equation of a parabola.

Example Write an equation for and graph a parabola with focus $(-4, -3)$ and vertex $(1, -3)$.

Because the focus and vertex share the same y-coordinate, the graph is horizontal. The focus is $(h + p, k)$, so the value of p is $-4 - 1$ or -5. Because p is negative, the graph opens to the left.

Write the equation for the parabola in standard form using the values of h, p, and k.

$(y - k)^2 = 4p(x - h)$ Standard form

$[y - (-3)]^2 = 4(-5)(x - 1)$ $p = -5$, $h = 1$, and $k = -3$

$(y + 3)^2 = -20(x - 1)$ Simplify.

The standard form of the equation is $(y + 3)^2 = -20(x - 1)$.

Graph the vertex, focus, and parabola.

Exercises

Write an equation for and graph a parabola with the given characteristics.

1. focus $(-1, 5)$ and vertex $(2, 5)$

$(y - 5)^2 = -12(x - 2)$

2. focus $(1, 4)$; opens down; contains $(-3, 1)$

$(x - 1)^2 = -4(y - 5)$

3. directrix $y = 6$; opens down; vertex $(5, 3)$

$(x - 5)^2 = -12(y - 3)$

4. focus $(1.5, 1)$; opens right; directrix $x = 0.5$

$2(x - 1) = (y - 1)^2$

Answers (Lesson 7-1)

7-1 Enrichment

Tilted Parabolas

The diagram at the right shows a fixed point $F(1, 1)$ and a line d that has an equation $y = -x - 2$. If $P(x, y)$ satisfies the condition that $PD = PF$, then P is on a parabola. Our objective is to find an equation for the tilted parabola, which is the locus of all points that are the same distance from $(1, 1)$ and the line $y = -x - 2$.

First find an equation for the line m through $P(x, y)$ and perpendicular to line d at $D(a, b)$. Using this equation and the equation for line d, find the coordinates (a, b) of point D in terms of x and y. Then use $(PD)^2 = (PF)^2$ to find an equation for the parabola.

Refer to the discussion above.

1. Find an equation for line m.

$$x - y + (b - a) = 0$$

2. Use the equations for lines m and d to show that the coordinates of point D are $D(a, b) = \left(\dfrac{x - y - 2}{2}, \dfrac{y - x - 2}{2} \right)$.

From the equation for line m,

$-a + b = -x + y$. **From the equation for line d,**

$a + b = -2$. **Subtract to get** $a = \dfrac{x - y - 2}{2}$.

Add to get $b = \dfrac{y - x - 2}{2}$.

3. Use the coordinates of F, P, and D, along with $(PD)^2 = (PF)^2$ to find an equation of the parabola with focus F and directrix d.

$$x^2 - 2xy + y^2 - 8x - 8y = 0$$

4. a. Every parabola has an axis of symmetry. Find an equation for the axis of symmetry of the parabola described above. Justify your answer.

$y = x$, **because** $y = x$ **contains** $F(1, 1)$ **and is perpendicular to** d.

b. Use your answer from part **a** to find the coordinates of the vertex of the parabola. Justify your answer.

$(0, 0)$, **because** $(0, 0)$ **is midway between point** F **and line** d.

7-1 Word Problem Practice

Parabolas

1. REFLECTOR The figure shows a parabolic reflecting mirror. A cross section of the mirror can be modeled by $x^2 = 16y$, where the values of x and y are measured in inches. Find the distance from the vertex to the focus of this mirror.

4 in.

2. T-SHIRTS The cheerleaders at the high school basketball game launch T-shirts into the stands after a victory. The launching device propels the shirts into the air at an initial velocity of 32 feet per second. A shirt's distance y in feet above the ground after x seconds can be modeled by $y = -16x^2 + 32x + 5$.

a. Write the equation in standard form.

$$(x - 1)^2 = -\frac{1}{16}(y - 21)$$

b. What is the maximum height that a T-shirt reaches?

21 ft

3. FLASHLIGHT A flashlight contains a parabolic mirror with a bulb in the center as a light source and focus. If the width of the height to the focus is 0.5 inch, find an equation of the parabolic cross section.

$$y = \frac{1}{2}x^2$$

4. ARCHWAYS The entrance to a college campus has a parabolic arch above two columns as shown in the figure.

a. Write an equation that models the parabola.

$$x^2 = -40y$$

b. Graph the equation.

5. BRIDGES The cable for a suspension bridge is in the shape of a parabola. The vertical supports are shown in the figure.

a. Write an equation for the parabolic cable.

$$x^2 = 800y$$

b. Find the length of a supporting wire that is 100 feet from the center.

22.5 ft

Answers

Answers (Lesson 7-2)

NAME _____ DATE _____ PERIOD _____

7-2 Study Guide and Intervention (continued)

Ellipses and Circles

Determine Types of Conic Sections If you are given the equation for a conic section, you can determine what type of conic is represented using the characteristics of the equation. The standard form of an equation for a circle with center (h, k) and radius r is $(x - h)^2 + (y - k)^2 = r^2$.

Example Write each equation in standard form. Identify the related conic.

a. $4x^2 + 9y^2 + 24x - 36y + 36 = 0$

$$4x^2 + 9y^2 + 24x - 36y + 36 = 0$$

$$4(x^2 + 6x + ?) + 9(y^2 - 4y + ?) = -36 + ? + ? \quad \text{Original equation}$$

$$4(x^2 + 6x + 9) + 9(y^2 - 4y + 4) = -36 + 36 + 36 \quad \text{Complete the square.}$$

$$4(x + 3)^2 + 9(y - 2)^2 = 36$$

$$\frac{(x + 3)^2}{9} + \frac{(y - 2)^2}{4} = 1 \quad \text{Divide each side by 36.}$$

Because the equation is of the form $\frac{(x - h)^2}{a^2} + \frac{(y - k)^2}{b^2} = 1$, the graph is an ellipse with center $(-3, 2)$.

b. $x^2 - 16x - 8y + 80 = 0$

$$x^2 - 16x - 8y + 80 = 0 \quad \text{Original equation}$$

$$(x^2 - 16x + ?) - 8y + 80 = 0$$

$$(x^2 - 16x + 64) - 8y + 80 - 64 = 0 \quad \text{Complete the square.}$$

$$(x - 8)^2 - 8(y - 2) = 0$$

$$(x - 8)^2 = 8(y - 2) \quad \text{Standard form}$$

Because only one term is squared, the graph is a parabola with vertex $(8, 2)$.

Exercises

Write each equation in standard form. Identify the related conic.

1. $y^2 + 2y + 6x^2 + 6x^2 - 24x - 24x = 5$

$$\frac{(y + 1)^2}{30} + \frac{(x - 2)^2}{5} = 1; \text{ ellipse}$$

2. $y^2 + 2y + x^2 - 24x = 14$

$$(x - 12)^2 + (y + 1)^2 = 169; \text{ circle}$$

3. $4x - 8 + y^2 + 4y = 0$

$$(y + 2)^2 = -4(x - 3); \text{ parabola}$$

4. $x^2 + 4x + y^2 - 2y - 49 = 0$

$$(x + 2)^2 + (y - 1)^2 = 54; \text{ circle}$$

5. $4x^2 + 8x + 5y^2 - 30y - 11 = 0$

$$\frac{(x + 1)^2}{15} + \frac{(y - 3)^2}{12} = 1; \text{ ellipse}$$

6. $6x^2 + 24x + 2y - 10 = 0$

$$(x + 2)^2 = -\frac{1}{3}(y - 17); \text{ parabola}$$

Chapter 7   11   Glencoe Precalculus

NAME _____ DATE _____ PERIOD _____

7-2 Study Guide and Intervention

Ellipses and Circles

Analyze and Graph Ellipses and Circles An ellipse is the locus of points in a plane such that the sum of the distances from two fixed points, called foci, is constant.

The standard form of the equation of an ellipse is $\frac{(x - h)^2}{a^2} + \frac{(y - k)^2}{b^2} = 1$ when the major axis is horizontal. In this case, a^2 is in the denominator of the x-term. The standard form is $\frac{(y - k)^2}{a^2} + \frac{(x - h)^2}{b^2} = 1$ when the major axis is vertical. In this case, a^2 is in the denominator of the y-term. In both cases, $c^2 = a^2 - b^2$.

Example Graph the ellipse given by the equation $\frac{(y - 1)^2}{25} + \frac{(x + 2)^2}{9} = 1$.

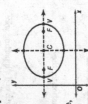

The equation is in standard form. Use the values of h, k, a, and b to determine the vertices and axes of the ellipse. Since $a^2 > b^2$, $a^2 = 25$ and $b^2 = 9$, or $a = 5$ and $b = 3$. Since a^2 is the denominator of the y-term, the major axis is parallel to the y-axis.

orientation:	vertical	
center:	$(-2, 1)$	(h, k)
vertices:	$(-2, 6), (-2, -4)$	$(h, k \pm a)$
co-vertices:	$(-5, 1), (1, 1)$	$(h \pm b, k)$
major axis:	$x = -2$	$x = h$
minor axis:	$y = 1$	$y = k$

Exercises

Graph the ellipse given by each equation.

1. $\frac{(x + 5)^2}{64} + \frac{(y + 2)^2}{25} = 1$

2. $\frac{(x + 2)^2}{25} + \frac{(y + 1)^2}{9} = 1$

3. $\frac{(y - 1)^2}{16} + \frac{(x + 3)^2}{9} = 1$

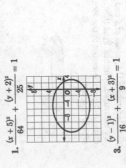

4. $\frac{(y + 3)^2}{64} + \frac{(x - 2)^2}{25} = 1$

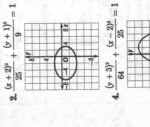

Chapter 7   10   Glencoe Precalculus

NAME _____ DATE _____ PERIOD _____

7-2 Practice

Ellipses and Circles

Graph the ellipse given by each equation.

1. $4x^2 + 9y^2 - 8x - 36y + 4 = 0$

2. $25x^2 + 9y^2 - 50x - 90y + 25 = 0$

Write an equation for the ellipse with each set of characteristics.

3. vertices $(-12, 6)$, $(4, 6)$; foci $(-10, 6)$, $(2, 6)$
$$\frac{(x+4)^2}{64} + \frac{(y-6)^2}{28} = 1$$

4. foci $(-2, 1)$, $(-2, 7)$; length of major axis 10 units
$$\frac{(y-4)^2}{25} + \frac{(x+2)^2}{16} = 1$$

Write each equation in standard form. Identify the related conic.

5. $y^2 - 4y = 4x + 16$
$(y-2)^2 = 4(x+5)$; parabola

6. $4x^2 - 32x + 3y^2 - 18y = -55$
$\frac{(x-4)^2}{9} + \frac{(y-3)^2}{12} = 1$; ellipse

7. $x^2 + y^2 - 8x - 24y = 9$
$(x-4)^2 + (y-12)^2 = 169$; circle

8. $x^2 + y^2 + 20x - 10y + 4 = 0$
$(x+10)^2 + (y-5)^2 = 121$; circle

Determine the eccentricity of the ellipse given by each equation.

9. $\frac{(x+1)^2}{25} + \frac{(y+1)^2}{16} = 1$
$\frac{3}{5}$

10. $\frac{(y+2)^2}{64} + \frac{(x+1)^2}{9} = 1$
$\frac{\sqrt{55}}{8}$

11. **CONSTRUCTION** A semi-elliptical arch is used to design a headboard for a bed frame. The headboard will have a height of 2 feet at the center and a width of 5 feet at the base. Where should the craftsman place the foci in order to sketch the arch?
1.5 ft to the sides of the center

NAME _____ DATE _____ PERIOD _____

7-2 Word Problem Practice

Ellipses and Circles

1. **WHISPERING GALLERY** A whispering gallery at a museum is in the shape of an ellipse. The room is 84 feet long and 46 feet wide.

   a. Write an equation modeling the shape of the room. Assume that it is centered at the origin and that the major axis is horizontal.
   $$\frac{x^2}{1764} + \frac{y^2}{529} = 1$$

   b. Find the location of the foci.
   ≈35 ft on either side of the center on the major axis

2. **SIGNS** A sign is in the shape of an ellipse. The eccentricity is 0.60 and the length is 48 inches.

   a. Write an equation for the ellipse if the center of the sign is at the origin and the major axis is horizontal.
   $$\frac{x^2}{576} + \frac{y^2}{368.64} = 1$$

   b. What is the maximum height of the sign?
   38.4 in.

3. **TUNNEL** The entrance to a tunnel is in the shape of half an ellipse as shown in the figure.

   a. Write an equation that models the ellipse.
   $$\frac{x^2}{400} + \frac{y^2}{225} = 1$$

   b. Find the height of the tunnel 10 feet from the center.
   ≈13 ft

4. **RETENTION POND** A circular retention pond is getting larger by overflowing and flooding the nearby land at a rate that increases the radius 100 yards per day, as shown below.

   a. Graph the circle that represents the water, and find the distance from the center of the pond to the house.
   ; 900 yd

   b. If the pond continues to overflow at the same rate, how many days will it take for the water to reach the house?
   7 days

   c. Write an equation for the circle of water at the current time and an equation for the circle when the water reaches the house.
   $x^2 + y^2 = 40,000$;
   $x^2 + y^2 = 810,000$

Answers

7-2 Graphing Calculator Activity

NAME _____ DATE _____ PERIOD _____

Translations of Ellipses

To graph an ellipse, such as $\frac{(x-3)^2}{18} + \frac{(y+2)^2}{32} = 1$, on a graphing calculator, you must first solve for y.

$$\frac{(x-3)^2}{18} + \frac{(y+2)^2}{32} = 1 \qquad \text{Original equation}$$

$$32(x-3)^2 + 18(y+2)^2 = 576 \qquad \text{Multiply each side by 576.}$$

$$18(y+2)^2 = 576 - 32(x-3)^2 \qquad \text{Subtract 32(x − 3)² from each side.}$$

$$(y+2)^2 = \frac{576 - 32(x-3)^2}{18} \qquad \text{Divide each side by 18.}$$

$$y = \pm\sqrt{\frac{576 - 32(x-3)^2}{18}} - 2 \qquad \text{Take the square root of each side.}$$

The result is two equations. To graph both equations in Y1, replace ± with {1, −1}. Be careful to include the proper parentheses or you will get an error message.

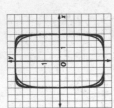

$\boxed{\text{Y=}}$ $\boxed{\text{2nd}}$ $\boxed{\{}$ $\boxed{1}$ $\boxed{,}$ $\boxed{(-)}$ $\boxed{1}$ $\boxed{\text{2nd}}$ $\boxed{\}}$ $\boxed{\sqrt{}}$ $\boxed{(}$ $\boxed{576}$ $\boxed{-}$ $\boxed{32}$ $\boxed{(}$ $\boxed{\text{X,T,θ,n}}$ $\boxed{-}$ $\boxed{3}$ $\boxed{)}$ $\boxed{x^2}$ $\boxed{)}$ $\boxed{\div}$ $\boxed{18}$ $\boxed{)}$ $\boxed{-}$ $\boxed{2}$ $\boxed{\text{ENTER}}$ $\boxed{\text{ZOOM}}$ 6.

Like other graphs, there are families of ellipses. Changing certain values in the equation of an ellipse creates a new member of that family.

Exercises

Graph each equation on a graphing calculator.   1–4. See students' work.

1. $\frac{(x-7)^2}{18} + \frac{(y+2)^2}{32} = 1$

2. $\frac{(x+1)^2}{18} + \frac{(y+2)^2}{32} = 1$

3. $\frac{(x-3)^2}{18} + \frac{(y-2)^2}{32} = 1$

4. $\frac{(x-3)^2}{18} + \frac{(y+6)^2}{32} = 1$

5. Describe the effects of replacing $x - 3$ in Exercises 3 and 4 with $(x \pm c)$ for $c > 0$.
Sample answer: the graph will move right or left.

6. Describe the effects of replacing $y + 2$ in Exercises 1 and 2 with $(y \pm c)$ for $c > 0$.
Sample answer: the graph will move up or down.

Chapter 7   15   Glencoe Precalculus

7-2 Enrichment

NAME _____ DATE _____ PERIOD _____

Superellipses

The circle and the ellipse are members of an interesting family of curves that were first studied by the French physicist and mathematician Gabriel Lamé (1795–1870). The general equation for the family is $\left|\frac{x}{a}\right|^n + \left|\frac{y}{b}\right|^n = 1$, with $a \neq 0$, $b \neq 0$, and $n > 0$.

For even values of n greater than 2, the curves are called superellipses.

1. Consider two curves that are not superellipses. Graph each equation on the grid at the right. State the type of curve produced each time.

a. $\left|\frac{x}{2}\right|^2 + \left|\frac{y}{2}\right|^2 = 1$ **circle**

b. $\left|\frac{x}{3}\right|^2 + \left|\frac{y}{2}\right|^2 = 1$ **ellipse**

2. In each of the following cases, you are given values of a, b, and n to use in the general equation. Write the resulting equation. Then graph. Sketch each graph on the grid at the right.

a. $a = 2, b = 3, n = 4$ $\left|\frac{x}{2}\right|^4 + \left|\frac{y}{3}\right|^4 = 1$

b. $a = 2, b = 3, n = 6$ $\left|\frac{x}{2}\right|^6 + \left|\frac{y}{3}\right|^6 = 1$

c. $a = 2, b = 3, n = 8$ $\left|\frac{x}{2}\right|^8 + \left|\frac{y}{3}\right|^8 = 1$

3. What shape will the graph of $\left|\frac{x}{2}\right|^n + \left|\frac{y}{3}\right|^n = 1$ approximate for greater and greater even, whole-number values of n?
a rectangle that is 6 units long and 4 units wide, centered at the origin

Chapter 7   14   Glencoe Precalculus

Left page

NAME _____ DATE _____ PERIOD _____

7-3 Study Guide and Intervention

Hyperbolas

Analyze and Graph Hyperbolas A hyperbola is the locus of all points in a plane such that the difference of their distances from two foci is constant. The standard form of the equation of a hyperbola is

$\dfrac{(x - h)^2}{a^2} - \dfrac{(y - k)^2}{b^2} = 1$ when the transverse axis is horizontal, and

$\dfrac{(y - k)^2}{a^2} - \dfrac{(x - h)^2}{b^2} = 1$ when the transverse axis is vertical. In both

cases, $a^2 + b^2 = c^2$.

Example Graph the hyperbola given by the equation $\dfrac{y^2}{16} - \dfrac{x^2}{4} = 1$.

The equation is in standard form. Both h and k are 0, so the center is at the origin. Because the x-term is subtracted, the transverse axis is vertical. Use the values of a, b, and c to determine the vertices and foci of the hyperbola.

Because $a^2 = 16$ and $b^2 = 4$, $a = 4$ and $b = 2$. Use the values of a and b to find the value of c.

$c^2 = a^2 + b^2$ Equation relating a, b, and c

$c^2 = 4^2 + 2^2$ $a = 4$ and $b = 2$

$c = \sqrt{20}$ or about 4.47   Simplify.

Determine the characteristics of the hyperbola.

center: $(0, 0)$ (h, k) foci: $(0, \sqrt{20}), (0, -\sqrt{20})$ $(h, k \pm c)$

vertices: $(0, 4), (0, -4)$ $(h, k \pm a)$ asymptotes: $y = 2x, y = -2x$ $y - k = \pm\dfrac{a}{b}(x - h)$

Make a table of values to sketch the hyperbola.

x	y
−2	−5.65, 5.65
−1	−4.5, 4.5
0	−4, 4
1	−4.5, 4.5
2	−5.65, 5.65

Exercises

Graph the hyperbola given by each equation.

1. $\dfrac{x^2}{25} - \dfrac{y^2}{36} = 1$

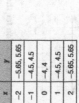

2. $\dfrac{(y - 3)^2}{25} - \dfrac{(x + 2)^2}{9} = 1$

3. $\dfrac{(x - 1)^2}{16} - \dfrac{(y + 2)^2}{36} = 1$

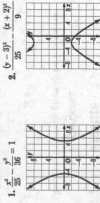

Right page

NAME _____ DATE _____ PERIOD _____

7-3 Study Guide and Intervention (continued)

Hyperbolas

Identify Conic Sections You can determine the type of conic when the equation for the conic is in general form, $Ax^2 + Bxy + Cy^2 + Dx + Ey + F = 0$. The discriminant, or $B^2 - 4AC$, can be used to identify a conic when the equation is in general form.

Discriminant	Conic Section
less than 0; $B = 0$ and $A = C$	circle
less than 0; $B \neq 0$ or $A \neq C$	ellipse
equal to 0	parabola
greater than 0	hyperbola

Example Use the discriminant to identify each conic section.

a. $2x^2 + 6y^2 - 8x + 12y - 2 = 0$

A is 2, B is 0, and C is 6. Find the discriminant.

$B^2 - 4AC = 0^2 - 4(2)(6)$ or −48

The discriminant is less than 0, so the conic must be either a circle or an ellipse. Because $A \neq C$, the conic is an ellipse.

b. $5x^2 + 8xy - 2y^2 + 4x - 3y + 10 = 0$

A is 5, B is 8, and C is −2. Find the discriminant.

$B^2 - 4AC = 8^2 - 4(5)(-2)$ or 104.

The discriminant is greater than 0, so the conic is a hyperbola.

c. $12x^2 + 12xy + 3y^2 - 7x + 2y - 6 = 0$

A is 12, B is 12, and C is 3. Find the discriminant.

$B^2 - 4AC = 12^2 - 4(12)(3)$ or 0

The discriminant is 0, so the conic is a parabola.

Exercises

Use the discriminant to identify each conic section.

1. $4x^2 + 4y^2 - 2x - 9y + 1 = 0$
   circle

2. $10x^2 + 6y^2 - x + 8y + 1 = 0$
   ellipse

3. $-2x^2 + 6xy + y^2 - 4x - 5y + 2 = 0$
   hyperbola

4. $x^2 + 6xy + y^2 - 2x + 1 = 0$
   hyperbola

5. $5x^2 + 2xy + 4y^2 + x + 2y + 17 = 0$
   ellipse

6. $x^2 + 2xy + y^2 + x + 10 = 0$
   parabola

7. $25x^2 + 100x - 54y = -200$
   parabola

8. $16x^2 + 100x - 54y^2 = -100$
   hyperbola

Answers (Lesson 7-3)

Panel 1 (Word Problem Practice)

7-3 Word Problem Practice

Hyperbolas

1. EARTHQUAKES The epicenter of an earthquake lies on a branch of the hyperbola represented by $\dfrac{(x-50)^2}{1600} - \dfrac{(y-35)^2}{2500} = 1$, where the seismographs are located at the foci.

a. Graph the hyperbola.

b. Find the locations of the seismographs.

$(-14, 35),\ (114, 35)$

2. SHADOWS A lamp projects light onto a wall in the shape of a hyperbola. The edge of the light can be modeled by $\dfrac{y^2}{196} - \dfrac{x^2}{121} = 1$.

a. Graph the hyperbola.

3. PARKS A grassy play area is in the shape of a hyperbola, as shown.

a. Write an equation that models the curved sides of the play area.

$\dfrac{(y-4)^2}{4} - \dfrac{(x-3)^2}{9} = 1$

b. If each unit on the coordinate plane represents 3 feet, what is the narrowest vertical width of the play area?

12 ft

4. SHADOWS The path of the shadow cast by the tip of a sundial is usually a hyperbola.

a. Write two equations of the hyperbola in standard form if the center is at the origin, given that the path contains a transverse axis of 24 millimeters with one focus 14 millimeters from the center.

$\dfrac{x^2}{144} - \dfrac{y^2}{52} = 1;\ \dfrac{y^2}{144} - \dfrac{x^2}{52} = 1$

b. Graph one hyperbola.

Sample answer:

Chapter 7   19   Glencoe Precalculus

Panel 2 (Practice)

7-3 Practice

Hyperbolas

Graph the hyperbola given by each equation.

1. $x^2 - 4y^2 - 4x + 24y - 36 = 0$

2. $\dfrac{y^2}{16} - \dfrac{(x-1)^2}{4} = 1$

Write an equation for the hyperbola with the given characteristics.

3. vertices $(-10, 6),\ (4, 6)$; foci $(-12, 6),\ (6, 6)$

$\dfrac{(x+3)^2}{49} - \dfrac{(y-6)^2}{32} = 1$

4. foci $(0, 6),\ (0, -4)$; length of transverse axis 8 units

$\dfrac{(y-1)^2}{16} - \dfrac{x^2}{9} = 1$

5. Determine the eccentricity of the hyperbola given by the equation $\dfrac{(x-7)^2}{36} - \dfrac{(y+10)^2}{121} = 1$.

$\dfrac{\sqrt{157}}{6}$

6. ENVIRONMENTAL NOISE Two neighbors who live one mile apart hear an explosion while they are talking on the telephone. One neighbor hears the explosion two seconds before the other. If sound travels at 1100 feet per second, determine the equation of the hyperbola on which the explosion was located.

$\dfrac{x^2}{1,210,000} - \dfrac{y^2}{5,759,600} = 1$

Use the discriminant to identify each conic section.

7. $5x^2 + xy + 2y^2 - 5x + 8y + 9 = 0$

ellipse

8. $16x^2 - 4y^2 - 8x - 8y + 1 = 0$

hyperbola

9. $4x^2 + 8xy + 4y^2 + x + 11y + 10 = 0$

parabola

10. $2x^2 + 4y^2 - 3x - 6y + 2 = 0$

ellipse

Chapter 7   18   Glencoe Precalculus

Answers (Lesson 7-3 and Lesson 7-4)

NAME _____ DATE _____ PERIOD _____

7-4 Study Guide and Intervention

Rotations of Conic Sections

Rotation of Conic Sections An equation $Ax^2 + Bxy + Cy^2 + Dx + Ey + F = 0$ in the xy-plane can be rewritten as $A(x')^2 + C(y')^2 + Dx' + Ey' + F = 0$ in the $x'y'$-plane by rotating the coordinate axes through an angle θ. The equation in the $x'y'$-plane can be found using $x = x' \cos\theta - y' \sin\theta$ and $y = x' \sin\theta + y' \cos\theta$.

Example Use $\theta = 45°$ to write the standard form of

$x^2 - 2xy - 4y^2 + \frac{1}{2} = 0$ in the $x'y'$-plane. Then identify the conic.

The conic is a hyperbola because $B^2 - 4AC > 0$. Find the equations for x and y.

Rotation equations for x and y

$\sin \frac{\pi}{4} = \frac{\sqrt{2}}{2}$ and $\cos \frac{\pi}{4} = \frac{\sqrt{2}}{2}$

$x = x' \cos\theta - y' \sin\theta \qquad\qquad y = x' \sin\theta + y' \cos\theta$

$= \frac{\sqrt{2}}{2}x' - \frac{\sqrt{2}}{2}y' \qquad\qquad = \frac{\sqrt{2}}{2}x' + \frac{\sqrt{2}}{2}y'$

Substitute into the original equation.

$x^2 \qquad - 2xy \qquad -4y^2 \qquad +\frac{1}{2} = 0$

$\left(\frac{\sqrt{2}x' - \sqrt{2}y'}{2}\right)^2 - 2\left(\frac{\sqrt{2}x' - \sqrt{2}y'}{2}\right)\left(\frac{\sqrt{2}x' + \sqrt{2}y'}{2}\right) - 4\left(\frac{\sqrt{2}x' + \sqrt{2}y'}{2}\right)^2 + \frac{1}{2} = 0$ Replace x and y.

$\frac{1}{2}(x')^2 - x'y' + \frac{1}{2}(y')^2 + (y')^2 - 2(x')^2 - 4x'y' - 2(y')^2 + \frac{1}{2} = 0$ Expand the binomials.

$-\frac{5}{2}(x')^2 - 5x'y' - \frac{1}{2}(y')^2 + \frac{1}{2} = 0$ Simplify.

The equation of the hyperbola after the $45°$ rotation is $5(x')^2 + 10x'y' + (y')^2 = 1$.

Exercises

Write each equation in the $x'y'$-plane for the given value of θ. Then identify the conic.

1. $x^2 - 4x + y^2 = 2$, $\theta = \frac{\pi}{4}$

$(x')^2 + (y')^2 - 2\sqrt{2}x' + 2\sqrt{2}y' - 2 = 0$; circle

2. $8x^2 - 5y^2 = 40$, $\theta = 30°$

$19(x')^2 - 26\sqrt{3}x'y' - 7(y')^2 = 160$; hyperbola

Chapter 7   21   *Glencoe Precalculus*

NAME _____ DATE _____ PERIOD _____

7-3 Enrichment

Moving Foci

Recall that the equation of a hyperbola with center at the origin and horizontal transverse axis has the equation $\frac{x^2}{a^2} - \frac{y^2}{b^2} = 1$. The foci are at $(-c, 0)$ and $(c, 0)$, where $c^2 = a^2 + b^2$, the vertices are at $(-a, 0)$ and $(a, 0)$, and the asymptotes have equations $y = \pm\frac{b}{a}x$. Such a hyperbola is shown at the right. What happens to the shape of the graph as c grows very large or very small?

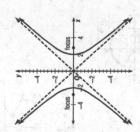

Refer to the hyperbola described above.

1. Write a convincing argument to show that as c approaches 0, the foci, the vertices, and the center of the hyperbola become the same point.

Because $0 < a < c$, as c approaches 0, a approaches 0. So the x-coordinates of the foci and vertices approach 0, which is the x-coordinate of the center. Because the y-coordinates are equal, the points become the same.

2. Use a graphing calculator or computer to graph $x^2 - y^2 = 1$, $x^2 - y^2 = 0.1$, and $x^2 - y^2 = 0.01$. (Such hyperbolas correspond to smaller and smaller values of c.) Describe the changes in the graphs. What shape do the graphs approach as c approaches 0?

The asymptotes remain the same, but the branches become sharper near the vertices.

The graphs approach the lines $y = x$ and $y = -x$.

3. Suppose a is held fixed and c approaches infinity. How does the graph of the hyperbola change?

The vertices remain at $(\pm a, 0)$, but the branches become more vertical. The graphs approach the vertical lines $x = -a$ and $x = a$.

4. Suppose b is held fixed and c approaches infinity. How does the graph of the hyperbola change?

The vertices recede to infinity and the branches become flatter and farther from the center. As c approaches infinity, the graphs tend to disappear.

Chapter 7   20   *Glencoe Precalculus*

7-4 Practice

Rotations of Conic Sections

Write each equation in the x'y'-plane for the given value of θ. Then identify the conic.

1. $xy = 1; \theta = \frac{\pi}{4}$

$\frac{1}{2}(x')^2 - \frac{1}{2}(y')^2 - 1 = 0$; hyperbola

2. $5x^2 + 6y^2 = 30; \theta = 30°$

$21(x')^2 + 2\sqrt{3}x'y' + 23(y')^2 - 120 = 0$; ellipse

Write an equation for each conic in the x'y'-plane for the given equation in x'y' form and the given value of θ.

3. $(x')^2 = 16(y'); \theta = 45°$

$x^2 + 16\sqrt{2}x + 2xy - 16\sqrt{2}y + y^2 = 0$

4. $\frac{(x')^2}{25} - \frac{(y')^2}{4} = 1; \theta = \frac{\pi}{3}$

$-71x^2 + 58\sqrt{3}xy - 13y^2 = 400$

Determine the angle θ through which the conic with each equation should be rotated. Then write the equation in standard form.

5. $x^2 + xy + y^2 = 2$

$45°; \frac{3(x')^2}{4} + \frac{(y')^2}{4} = 1$

6. $13x^2 - 8xy + 7y^2 - 45 = 0$

$63°; \frac{(x')^2}{9} + \frac{(y')^2}{3} = 1$

7. $16x^2 - 24xy + 9y^2 - 30x - 40y = 0$

$53°; (y')^2 = 2x'$

8. $18x^2 + 12xy + 13y^2 - 198 = 0$

$33.7°; \frac{(x')^2}{9} + \frac{(y')^2}{22} = 1$

9. **COMMUNICATIONS** Suppose the orientation of a satellite dish that monitors radio waves is modeled by the equation $4x^2 + 2xy + 4y^2 + \sqrt{2}x - \sqrt{2}y = 0$. What is the angle of rotation of the satellite dish about the origin?

45°

10. Graph $(x' + 1)^2 = -16(y' + 3)$ if it has been rotated 45° from its position in the xy-plane.

7-4 Study Guide and Intervention (continued)

Rotations of Conic Sections

Graph Rotated Conics When the equations of rotated conics are given for the xy-plane, they can be graphed by finding points on the graph of the conic and then converting these points to the xy-plane.

Example Graph $\frac{(x')^2}{36} + \frac{(y')^2}{64} = 1$ if it has been rotated 30° from its position in the xy-plane.

The equation represents an ellipse, and it is in standard form. Use the center (0, 0); the vertices (0, 8), (0, −8); and the co-vertices (6, 0), (−6, 0) to determine the center and vertices for the ellipse in the xy-plane.

Find the equations for x and y for θ = 30°.

$x = x' \cos \theta - y' \sin \theta$ Rotation equations for x and y

$= \frac{\sqrt{3}}{2}x' - \frac{1}{2}y'$ sin 30° = $\frac{1}{2}$ and cos 30° = $\frac{\sqrt{3}}{2}$

$y = x' \sin \theta + y' \cos \theta$

$= \frac{1}{2}x' + \frac{\sqrt{3}}{2}y'$

Use the equations to convert the x'y'-coordinates of the center into xy-coordinates.

$x = \frac{\sqrt{3}}{2}(0) - \frac{1}{2}(0)$ $y = \frac{1}{2}(0) + \frac{\sqrt{3}}{2}(0)$

$= 0$ $= 0$ $x' = 0$ and $y' = 0$ Multiply.

Likewise, convert the coordinates of the vertices and co-vertices into xy-coordinates.

$(0, 8) \to (-4, 4\sqrt{3})$ $(0, -8) \to (4, -4\sqrt{3})$ $(6, 0) \to (3\sqrt{3}, 3)$ $(-6, 0) \to (-3\sqrt{3}, -3)$

The new center, vertices, and co-vertices can be used to sketch the graph of the ellipse in the xy-plane.

Exercises

Graph each equation at the indicated angle.

1. $(x' + 6)^2 = 12(y' + 2); \frac{\pi}{2}$

2. $\frac{(x')^2}{9} - \frac{(y')^2}{4} = 1; 60°$

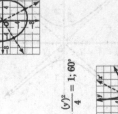

NAME _____ DATE _____ PERIOD _____

7-4 Enrichment

Graphing with Addition of y-Coordinates

Equations of parabolas, ellipses, and hyperbolas that are "tipped" with respect to the x- and y-axes are more difficult to graph than the equations you have been studying.

Often, however, you can use the graphs of two simpler equations to graph a more complicated equation. For example, the graph of the ellipse in the diagram at the right is obtained by adding the y-coordinate of each point on the circle and the y-coordinate of the corresponding point of the line.

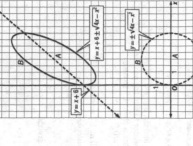

$y = x + 6$

$y = x + 6 \pm \sqrt{4x - x^2}$

$y = \pm\sqrt{4x - x^2}$

Graph each equation. State the type of curve for each graph.

1. $y = 6 - x \pm \sqrt{4 - x^2}$ **ellipse**

$y = 6 - x$

$y = 6 - x \pm \sqrt{4 - x^2}$

$y = \pm\sqrt{4 - x^2}$

2. $y = x \pm \sqrt{x}$ **parabola**

$y = x \pm \sqrt{x}$

$y = x + \sqrt{x}$

$y = \pm\sqrt{x}$

Use a separate sheet of graph paper to graph these equations. State the type of curve for each graph.

3. $y = 2x \pm \sqrt{7 + 6x - x^2}$ **ellipse;**   **See students' graphs.**

4. $y = -2x \pm \sqrt{-2x}$ **parabola;**   **See students' graphs.**

Chapter 7   25   Glencoe Precalculus

NAME _____ DATE _____ PERIOD _____

7-4 Word Problem Practice

Rotations of Conic Sections

1. **COMMUNICATIONS** A satellite dish is modeled by the equation $y = \frac{1}{8}x^2$ when it is directly overhead. Later in the day, the dish has rotated 60°.

   a. Write an equation that models the new orientation of the satellite dish.

   $$\frac{(x')^2}{32} - \frac{\sqrt{3}}{16}x'y' + \frac{3}{32}y'^2 - \frac{\sqrt{3}}{2}x' - \frac{1}{2}y' = 0$$

   b. Draw the graph.

2. **GEARS** Suppose the equation of an elliptical gear rotated 60° in the xy'-plane is $\frac{(x')^2}{16} + \frac{(y')^2}{20} = 1$.

   a. Write an equation for the ellipse formed by the gear in the xy-plane.

   $$17x^2 + 2\sqrt{3}xy + 19y^2 - 320 = 0$$

   b. Draw the graph.

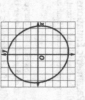

3. **ART** Mimi is drawing a picture with rotated parabolas. She wants to graph $(x' - 3)^2 = 12(y' - 4)$ if it has been rotated 45° from the xy-plane.

   a. Find the vertex in the xy-plane.

   $$\left(-\frac{\sqrt{2}}{2}, \frac{7\sqrt{2}}{2}\right)$$

   b. Find the equation for the axis of symmetry in the xy-plane.

   $$y = 3\sqrt{2} - x$$

   c. Draw the graph in the xy-plane.

4. **LOGIC** A hyperbola has been rotated 40° clockwise. Through what angle must it be rotated to return it to its original position?

   40° counterclockwise

5. **SHAPES** The shape of a reflecting mirror in a telescope can be modeled by $25x^2 + 13xy + 2y^2 = 100$. Determine whether the reflector is elliptical, parabolic, or hyperbolic.

   elliptical

Chapter 7   24   Glencoe Precalculus

Answers (Lesson 7-5)

Page 27

NAME _____ DATE _____ PERIOD _____

7-5 Study Guide and Intervention (continued)

Parametric Equations

Projectile Motion Parametric equations are often used to simulate projectile motion. For an object launched at an angle θ with the horizontal at an initial velocity v_0, where g is the gravitational constant, t is time, and h_0 is the initial height, the horizontal distance x can be found by $x = tv_0 \cos \theta$ and the vertical position y by $y = tv_0 \sin \theta - \frac{1}{2}gt^2 + h_0$.

Example Luigi is kicking a soccer ball. He kicks the ball with an initial velocity of 35 feet per second at an angle of 48° with the horizontal. The ball is 2 feet above the ground when he kicks it. How far will the ball travel horizontally before it hits the ground?

Step 1 Make a diagram of the situation.

35 ft/sec
48°
2 ft

Step 2 Write a parametric equation for the vertical position of the ball.

$y = tv_0 \sin \theta - \frac{1}{2}gt^2 + h_0$ Parametric equation for vertical position

$= t(35) \sin (48) - \frac{1}{2}(32)t^2 + 2$ $v_0 = 35, \theta = 48°, g = 32, \text{ and } h_0 = 2$

Step 3 Graph the equation for the vertical position and the line $y = 0$. Use **5: INTERSECT** on the **CALC** menu of a calculator to find the point of intersection of the curve with $y = 0$. The value is about 1.7 seconds. You could also use **2: ZERO** and not graph $y = 0$.

Step 4 Determine the horizontal position of the ball at 1.7 seconds.

$x = tv_0 \cos \theta$ Parametric equation for horizontal position

$= 1.7(35) \cos 48$ $v_0 = 35, \theta = 48°, \text{ and } t = 1.7$

≈ 39.8 Use a calculator.

The ball will travel about 39.8 feet before it hits the ground.

Exercises

1. Julie is throwing a ball at an initial velocity of 28 feet per second and an angle of 56° with the horizontal from a height of 4 feet. How far away will the ball land? **about 25 ft**

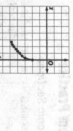

2. Jerome hits a tennis ball at an initial velocity of 38 feet per second and an angle of 42° with the horizontal from a height of 1.5 feet. How far away will the ball land if it is not hit by his opponent? **about 46.6 ft**

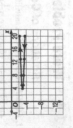

Chapter 7   27   *Glencoe Precalculus*

Page 26

NAME _____ DATE _____ PERIOD _____

7-5 Study Guide and Intervention

Parametric Equations

Graph Parametric Equations Parametric equations are used to describe the horizontal and vertical components of an equation. **Parameters** are arbitrary values, usually time or angle measurement.

Example 1 Sketch the curve given by the parametric equations $x = -3 + 4t$ and $y = t^2 + 3$ over the interval $-4 \leq t \leq 4$.

Make a table of values for $-4 \leq t \leq 4$. Plot the (x, y) coordinates for each t-value and connect the points to form a smooth curve.

t	x	y
-4	-19	19
-3	-15	12
-2	-11	7
-1	-7	4
0	-3	3
1	1	4
2	5	7
3	9	12
4	13	19

Example 2 Write $x = 4t - 2$ and $y = t^2 + 1$ in rectangular form.

$x = 4t - 2$ Parametric equation for x

$\frac{x + 2}{4} = t$ Solve for t.

$y = \left(\frac{x + 2}{4}\right)^2 + 1$ Substitute $\frac{x + 2}{4}$ for t in the equation for y.

$= \frac{x^2 + 4x + 4}{16} + 1$ Square $\frac{x + 2}{4}$.

$= \frac{x^2}{16} + \frac{x}{4} + \frac{5}{4}$ Simplify.

The rectangular equation is $y = \frac{x^2}{16} + \frac{x}{4} + \frac{5}{4}$.

Exercises

Sketch the curve given by each pair of parametric equations over the given interval.

1. $x = t^2 + 4$ and $y = \frac{t}{6} - 3$; $-4 \leq t \leq 4$

2. $x = \frac{t}{3}$ and $y = \sqrt{t} + 2$; $0 \leq t \leq 8$

Chapter 7   26   *Glencoe Precalculus*

NAME _____ DATE _____ PERIOD _____

7-5 Word Problem Practice

Parametric Equations

1. PHYSICS A rock is thrown at an initial velocity of 5 meters per second at an angle of 8° with the ground. After 0.4 second, how far has the rock traveled horizontally?

1.98 m

2. PLAYING CATCH Tom and Sarah are playing catch. Tom tosses a ball to Sarah at an initial velocity of 38 feet per second at an angle of 28° from a height of 4 feet. Sarah is 40 feet away from Tom.

a. How high above the ground will the ball be when it gets to Sarah?

2.53 ft

b. What is the maximum height of the ball?

8.97 ft

3. TENNIS Melinda hits a tennis ball with an initial velocity of 42 feet per second at an angle of 16° with the horizontal from a height of 2 feet. She is 20 feet from the net and the net is 3 feet high. Will the ball go over the net?

Yes, at 20 feet the ball is about 3.8 feet above the ground.

4. BASKETBALL Mandy throws a basketball with an initial velocity of 28 feet per second at an angle of 60° with the horizontal. If Mandy releases the ball from a height of 5 feet, write a pair of equations to determine the vertical and horizontal positions of the ball.

vertical: $y = t(28) \sin (60)$
$- 16t^2 + 5$;

horizontal: $x = t(28) \cos (60)$

5. GOLF Julio hit a golf ball with an initial velocity of 100 feet per second at an angle of 39° with the horizontal.

a. Write parametric equations for the flight of the ball.

$x = 100t \cos 39°$,
$y = 100t \sin 39° - 16t^2$

b. Find the maximum height the ball reaches.

about 61.9 ft

6. BASEBALL Micah hit a baseball at an initial velocity of 120 feet per second from a height of 3 feet at an angle of 34°.

a. How far will the ball travel horizontally before it hits the ground?

421.6 ft

b. What is the maximum height the ball will reach?

73.36 ft

c. If the fence is 8 feet tall and 400 feet from home plate, will the ball clear the fence to be a home run? Explain.

Sample answer: Yes; at 400 ft the ball is 15.4 feet above the ground so it will clear the fence.

NAME _____ DATE _____ PERIOD _____

7-5 Practice

Parametric Equations

Sketch the curve given by each pair of parametric equations over the given interval.

1. $x = t^2 + 1$ and $y = \frac{t}{2} - 6$; $-5 \le t \le 5$

2. $x = 2t + 6$ and $y = -\frac{t^2}{2}$; $-5 \le t \le 5$

Write each pair of parametric equations in rectangular form.

3. $x = 2t + 3, y = t - 4$

$y = \frac{1}{2}x - \frac{11}{2}$

4. $x = t + 5, y = -3t^2$

$y = -3(x - 5)^2$

5. $x = 3 \sin \theta, y = 2 \cos \theta$

$\frac{x^2}{9} + \frac{y^2}{4} = 1$

6. $y = 4 \sin \theta, x = 5 \cos \theta$

$\frac{y^2}{16} + \frac{x^2}{25} = 1$

Use each parameter to write the parametric equations that can represent each equation. Then graph the equation, indicating the speed and orientation.

7. $t = \frac{2 - x}{3}$ for $y = \frac{3 - x^2}{2}$

8. $t = 4x - 1$ for $y = x^2 + 2$

9. MODEL ROCKETRY Manuel launches a toy rocket from ground level with an initial velocity of 80 feet per second at an angle of 80° with the horizontal.

a. Write parametric equations to represent the path of the rocket.

$x = 80t \cos 80°; y = 80t \sin 80° - 16t^2$

b. How long will it take the rocket to travel 10 feet horizontally from its starting point? What will be its vertical distance at that point?

0.72 s; 48.43 ft

Answers (Lesson 7-5)

7-5 Spreadsheet Activity

Parametric Equations

You have learned that the motion of orbiting planets can be modeled using parametric equations. A spreadsheet can be used to evaluate parametric equations and to provide a graph of a planet's orbit.

Use the parametric equations for Saturn's position in its orbit in a spreadsheet. To calculate the x position, enter the following formula in B2: = 9.5*COS(PI()15*A2). To calculate the y position, enter the formula = 9.48*SIN(PI()15*A2) in C2. Use the fill handle to paste these formulas into the remaining cells in columns B and C.

	A	B	C
1	t	x	y
2	2	8.676882	3.855863
3	4	6.356741	7.045013
4	6	2.93661	9.016016
5	8	-0.99302	9.428068
6	10	-4.75	8.209921

In the spreadsheet, the values in column A represent t, and the values in columns B and C represent the calculated x and y values of Saturn's position at time t.

Exercises

1. Complete the spreadsheet to find the position of Saturn every 2 years from $t = 2$ to $t = 32$. Use the spreadsheet to make an X-Y graph of Saturn's position.

2. Find the coordinates representing Saturn's position after 23 years.

   (0.97, −9.43)

3. Given the parametric equations $x = 6 \sin 3t$ and $y = -4 \cos t$, write the formulas to put into your spreadsheet if time is found in cell A2.

   = 6*SIN(A2*3) and
   = −4*COS(A2)

7-5 Enrichment

Coordinate Equations of Projectiles

The path of a projectile after it is launched is a parabola when graphed on a coordinate plane.

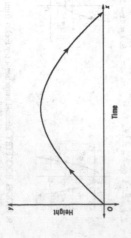

The path assumes that gravity is the only force acting on the projectile.

The equation of the path of a projectile on the coordinate plane is given by

$$y = -\left(\frac{g}{2v_0{}^2 \cos^2\alpha}\right)x^2 + (\tan \alpha)x,$$

where g is the acceleration due to gravity, 9.8 m/s² or 32 ft/s², v_0 is the initial velocity, and α is the angle at which the projectile is fired.

Example   Write the equation of a projectile fired at an angle of 10° to the horizontal with an initial velocity of 120 m/s.

$$y = -\left(\frac{9.8}{2(120)^2 \cos^2 10°}\right)x^2 + (\tan 10°)x$$

$$y = -0.00035x^2 + 0.18x$$

Find the equation of the path of each projectile.

1. a projectile fired at 80° to the horizontal with an initial velocity of 200 ft/s

   $y = -0.013x^2 + 5.67x$

2. a projectile fired at 40° to the horizontal with an initial velocity of 150 m/s

   $y = -0.00037x^2 + 0.84x$

Chapter 7 Assessment Answer Key

Quiz 1 (Lessons 7-1 and 7-2)
Page 33

1. $\dfrac{(y+1)^2}{16}+\dfrac{(x-3)^2}{4}=1$; ellipse

2.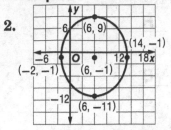

3. $(2,-1)$; $(2,-3)$; $x=2$; $y=1$

4. $\dfrac{(x+2)^2}{36}+\dfrac{(y-5)^2}{11}=1$

5. _____D_____

Quiz 2 (Lesson 7-3)
Page 33

1.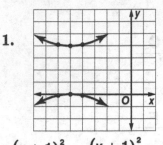

2. $\dfrac{(x+1)^2}{9}-\dfrac{(y+1)^2}{7}=1$

3. $\dfrac{6\sqrt{2}}{11}$

4. hyperbola

5. _____D_____

Quiz 3 (Lesson 7-4)
Page 34

1. hyperbola; $x'^2 - 4x'y' - y'^2 - 12 = 0$

2. ellipse; $31(x')^2 - 10\sqrt{3}x'y' + 21(y')^2 - 144 = 0$

3. _____14°_____

4. $11x^2 - 10\sqrt{3}xy + y^2 + 144 = 0$

5. _____D_____

Quiz 4 (Lesson 7-5)
Page 34

1.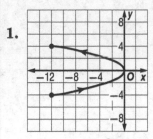

2. $\dfrac{x^2}{25}+\dfrac{y^2}{49}=1$

3. _____D_____

4. $x = 65t\cos 35°$, $y = 65t\sin 35° - 16t^2$; yes

5. about 2.33 s

Mid-Chapter Test
Page 35

1. _____B_____

2. _____F_____

3. _____B_____

4. _____H_____

5. $\dfrac{(y-1)^2}{16}-\dfrac{(x-2)^2}{25}=1$

6. $x^2 = -32y$

7.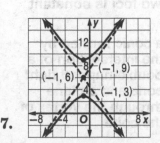

Chapter 7 Assessment Answer Key

Vocabulary Test
Page 36

Form 1
Page 37

Page 38

1. _____ true _____

2. false; $a^2 - b^2 = c^2$

3. _____ true _____

4. false; greater than

5. false; transverse axis

6. false; parametric

7. _____ true _____

8. false; perpendicular

9. _____ true _____

10. false; $\pm\dfrac{a}{b}$

11. the set of all points in a plane such that the difference of their distances from two foci is constant

12. a conic formed by the intersection of a double-napped right cone and a plane through the vertex of the cone

1. ___B___

2. ___F___

3. ___C___

4. ___G___

5. ___C___

6. ___H___

7. ___A___

8. ___F___

9. ___D___

10. ___H___

11. ___B___

12. ___G___

13. ___B___

14. ___J___

15. ___C___

16. ___F___

17. ___C___

18. ___F___

B: $y = 4x - 4$

Chapter 7 Assessment Answer Key

Form 2A
Page 39

Page 40

Form 2B
Page 41

Page 42

1. __B__

2. __H__

3. __A__

4. __G__

5. __A__

6. __G__

7. __A__

8. __G__

9. __B__

10. __J__

11. __D__

12. __J__

13. __D__

14. __J__

15. __B__

16. __F__

17. __B__

18. __F__

B: $y = -\dfrac{1}{2}x - 2$

1. __D__

2. __G__

3. __B__

4. __H__

5. __C__

6. __G__

7. __A__

8. __J__

9. __A__

10. __J__

11. __D__

12. __F__

13. __C__

14. __H__

15. __C__

16. __J__

17. __D__

18. __J__

B: $y = x - 3$

Answers

Chapter 7 Assessment Answer Key

1. $(-4, 1)$

2. $(-4, 3), (-4, -1)$

3. $(-4 \pm 2\sqrt{2}, 1),$
   $(-4, 1 \pm 2\sqrt{3})$

4. $27°$

5. $\dfrac{x^2}{64} + \dfrac{y^2}{4} = 1$

6. $x = \dfrac{t + 3}{2},$
   $y = \dfrac{t^2 + 6t + 13}{4}$

7. $\dfrac{(x')^2}{3} + (y')^2 = 1$

8. $x = 100t \cos 35°,$
   $y = 100t \sin 35°$
   $+ 4 - 16t^2$

9. Sample answer:
   $x^2 = -48y$

10. $(9, 6 \pm \sqrt{145})$

11. $y - 6 = \pm\dfrac{8}{9}(x - 9)$

12. $\dfrac{(y + 3)^2}{3} - \dfrac{(x + 2)^2}{9} = 1$

13. $(-6, 1), y = 1$

14. $(x + 2)^2 = -20(y - 1)$

15. hyperbola

16.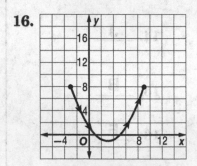

17. about 0.7 s

18. about 32.1 ft

19. hyperbola

20. $(x - 2)^2 +$
    $(y - 7)^2 = 225$

B: $\dfrac{(x - 2)^2}{9} + \dfrac{(y + 5)^2}{4} = 1$

Chapter 7 Assessment Answer Key

Form 2D
Page 45

1. $(3, -1)$

2. $(3 \pm \sqrt{5}, -1)$

3. $(6, -1), (0, -1),$ $(3, 1), (3, -3)$

4. $63°$

5. $\dfrac{x^2}{100} + \dfrac{y^2}{9} = 1$

6. $x = \dfrac{t - 4}{2},$ $y = \dfrac{t^2 - 8t + 24}{4}$

7. $\dfrac{(x')^2}{2} + \dfrac{(y')^2}{26} = 1$

8. $x = 110t \cos 32°,$ $y = 110t \sin 32°$ $+ 3 - 16t^2$

9. $x^2 = -60y$

10. $(-3 \pm \sqrt{5}, 2)$

11. $y - 2 = \pm 2(x + 3)$

Page 46

12. $\dfrac{(y + 2)^2}{4} - \dfrac{(x + 1)^2}{16} = 1$

13. $(2, 1), y = 1$

14. $(x - 2)^2 = -16(y + 5)$

15. hyperbola

16.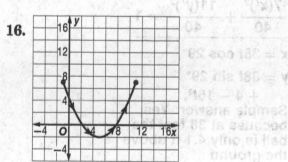

17. about 0.62 s

18. about 34.6 ft

19. ellipse

20. $(x + 6)^2 +$ $(y + 9)^2 = 121$

B: $\dfrac{(x + 4)^2}{25} + \dfrac{(y - 1)^2}{4} = 1$

Answers

Chapter 7 Assessment Answer Key

Form 3
Page 47

1. $(-3, 2)$

2. $(-3, 2 \pm \sqrt{5})$

3. $(-3, 5), (-3, -1),$ $(-1, 2), (-5, 2)$

4. hyperbola; 2°

5. $\dfrac{x^2}{4} + \dfrac{y^2}{9} = 1$

6. $x = \dfrac{t + 2}{3},$ $y = \dfrac{-t^2 - 4t + 32}{9}$

7. $\dfrac{7(x')^2}{40} + \dfrac{11(y')^2}{40} = 1$

8. $x = 38t \cos 29°,$ $y = 38t \sin 29°$ $+ 4 - 16t^2;$ Sample answer: Yes, because at 38 feet the ball is only 4.1 ft above the ground

9. Sample answer: $x^2 = -\dfrac{125}{3}y$

10. $(-1 \pm 2\sqrt{5}, -2)$

11. $y + 2 = \pm 2(x + 1)$

Page 48

12. $\dfrac{(x + 2)^2}{25} - \dfrac{(y - 4)^2}{16} = 1$

13. $(2, -2), y = -2$

14. $(y + 5)^2 = -40(x - 2)$

15. hyperbola

16.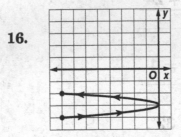

17. about 0.68 ft

18. Sample answer: Yes, when the ball is 20 feet in front of her it is at a height of 0.94 feet.

19. $\dfrac{\sqrt{2}}{2}$

20. $(x - 13)^2 +$ $(y - 12)^2 = 325$

B: $\dfrac{(x + 1)^2}{625} + \dfrac{(y - 3)^2}{400} = 1$

Chapter 7 Assessment Answer Key

1a. The equation is a circle if $A = B$.
Sample answer:
$(x - 1)^2 + (y - 2)^2 = 4$

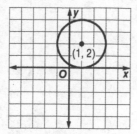

1b. The equation is an ellipse if $A \neq B$ and A and B have the same sign.
Sample answer:
$$\frac{(x + 2)^2}{4} + \frac{(y - 1)^2}{1} = 1$$

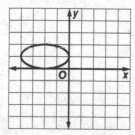

1c. The equation is a parabola when A or B is zero, but not both.
Sample answer: $y - 2 = 4(x + 1)^2$

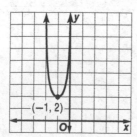

1d. The equation is a hyperbola if A and B have opposite signs. Sample answer:
$$\frac{y^2}{4} - \frac{x^2}{1} = 1$$

1e. The graph is an ellipse since
$(-1)^2 - 4(3)(2) < 0$.
$\cot 2\theta = \dfrac{3 - 2}{-1} = -1$, $2\theta = 135°$,
$\theta \approx 68°$

2a. The graph of $x^2 - 4y^2 = 0$ is two lines of slope $\dfrac{1}{2}$ and slope $-\dfrac{1}{2}$ that intersect at the origin.
$$x^2 - 4y^2 = 0$$
$$x^2 = 4y^2$$
$$|x| = 2|y|$$
$$\frac{|x|}{2} = |y|$$
$$\frac{x}{2} = y \text{ or } \frac{-x}{2} = y$$

2b.

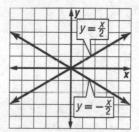

2c. degenerate hyperbola

3. Sample answer: Most lamps with circular shades shine a cone of light. When this light cone strikes a nearby wall, the resulting shape is a hyperbola. The hyperbola is formed by the cone of light intersecting the plane of the wall.

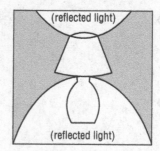

Answers

Chapter 7 Assessment Answer Key

Standardized Test Practice
Page 50

Page 51

1. Ⓐ Ⓑ Ⓒ ●

2. Ⓕ Ⓖ ● Ⓙ

3. ● Ⓑ Ⓒ Ⓓ

4. Ⓕ Ⓖ ● Ⓙ

5. Ⓐ Ⓑ ● Ⓓ

6. Ⓕ ● Ⓗ Ⓙ

7. Ⓐ Ⓑ Ⓒ ●

8. ● Ⓖ Ⓗ Ⓙ

9. Ⓐ Ⓑ ● Ⓓ

10. ● Ⓖ Ⓗ Ⓙ

11. ● Ⓑ Ⓒ Ⓓ

12. Ⓕ Ⓖ ● Ⓙ

13. Ⓐ ● Ⓒ Ⓓ

14. Ⓕ ● Ⓗ Ⓙ

15. ● Ⓑ Ⓒ Ⓓ

16. Ⓕ ● Ⓗ Ⓙ

17. Ⓐ Ⓑ Ⓒ ●

18. Ⓕ Ⓖ Ⓗ ●

19. Ⓐ ● Ⓒ Ⓓ

Chapter 7 Assessment Answer Key

20. $\dfrac{x^2}{100} + \dfrac{y^2}{16} = 1$

21.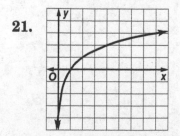

22. $(x - 4)^2 = 8(y - 9)$

23. $26.57°,$
$5(x')^2 - \sqrt{5}\,y' = 13$

24. $(1, -4)$

25. 25.4 mi

26. $\dfrac{\log_4 6}{\log_4 e}$

27. $(-4, 1), (3, \infty)$

28a. $x = 85t \cos 34°,$
$y = 85t \sin 34° +$
$3 - 16t^2$

28b. about 38.3 ft

28c. about 213.5 ft